METHADONE MAINTENANCE:
A Technological Fix

Other books by Dorothy Nelkin in
THE SCIENCE, TECHNOLOGY, AND SOCIETY SERIES

Nuclear Power and Its Critics:
The Cayuga Lake Controversy

The Politics of Housing Information:
The Fate of the Civilian Industrial Technology Program

The University and Military Research:
Moral Politics at M.I.T.

Methadone Maintenance:
A Technological Fix

FURTHER VOLUMES IN PREPARATION

METHADONE MAINTENANCE:
A Technological Fix

DOROTHY NELKIN

George Braziller   New York

For information, address the publisher:
George Braziller, Inc.
One Park Avenue, New York, N.Y. 10016

Standard Book Number: 0–8076–0681–2, cloth
0–8076–0680–4, paper

Library of Congress Catalog Card Number: 72–96071

FIRST PRINTING
Printed in the United States of America

Acknowledgments

A study of this kind requires the cooperation of a great many people. I am much indebted to those who responded to lengthy interviews and provided information and advice based on their experience in drug rehabilitation and related programs in Syracuse and elsewhere. These included the patients as well as the staff of various programs. In addition, I wish to acknowledge the cooperation of respondants from the New York State Employment Service, the Onondaga County Legislature, the Syracuse Coordinating Committee on Drug Abuse, and St. Joseph's Hospital administration. This book could not have been written without their willing cooperation. I would especially like to thank the staff of the Syracuse Methadone Maintenance Program. Dr. Robert E. Pittenger, M.D., Earleen Foulk and others generously gave their time to provide data and to share their insights. I am grateful to Ronald Dougherty, M.D., and the participants in the Thursday meetings for permission to attend their discussions, and to the Onondaga County Department of Mental Health for providing data.

Drafts of the manuscript were criticized by Harvey Brooks, Earleen Foulk, Christine Gianopoulos, Alfred

Lindesmith, Robert Morison, M.D., Marie Provine, Michael Reagen, Richard Remp, Judith Reppy, and Andrew Sorenson. Their comments were invaluable in checking accuracy, in maintaining perspective, and in developing the analysis. All readers were not always in agreement with the views expressed in these chapters; responsibility naturally rests with the author.

The research, editorial, and typing assistance of Donna Coggshall, Susan Mackenzie, Mary Ann Rygiel, and Sidney Siskin is warmly appreciated. Finally, I am indebted to the National Science Foundation for support in the research and writing of this study.

D.N.

Ithaca, New York

Contents

Tables

SCIENCE, TECHNOLOGY, AND SOCIETY

METHADONE
MAINTENANCE:
A Technological Fix

Introduction

To what extent can social problems be circumvented by reducing them to technological problems? Can we identify quick technological fixes for profound and almost infinitely complicated social problems, fixes that are within the grasp of modern technology and which would either eliminate the original social problem without requiring a change in the individual's social attitudes or would alter the problem as to make its resolution more feasible?[1]

As heroin addiction and the criminal network sustaining it are increasingly seen as a major threat to social order in the United States, a system of narcotics politics has developed that includes law enforcement agencies, a regulatory system, and programs to rehabilitate the heroin addict. Methadone maintenance, essentially a chemotherapeutic "fix" for heroin addiction, has become the predominant means of dealing with the poorly understood problems of the addict and the social consequences of addiction. In the spring of 1972, there were over 65,000 addicts in 450 methadone maintenance programs throughout the United States.

Methadone is a synthetic, addictive opiate used as a substitute for heroin. In 1963 it was discovered that dependence on heroin can be transferred to methadone.

Given a daily oral dose of methadone, an addict can be stabilized, or "maintained," in a condition where his physical yearning for heroin is eliminated. While still addicted to a drug, he is free from the necessity of continued "hustling" to meet his physiological need for heroin. Although, as we shall see, the physiological effect of methadone is similar to that of heroin, for society methadone maintenance has been heralded as a hopeful breakthrough in the effort to reduce the growing problem of addiction-related crime.

For the addict, once he decides to seek help, the availability of methadone provides a relief. According to Marie Nyswander, one of the founders of methadone maintenance treatment, "When an addict no longer has to worry compulsively about his source of supply, then he can concentrate on other things. At that point rehabilitation can become a meaningful word."[2] Thus, while the essence of methadone maintenance is the substitution of one addictive drug that is legal for another that is illegal, the provision of this drug is intended only as the basis for a complex rehabilitation routine.

The controversial development of methadone maintenance and the problems of individual programs suggest the complex issues involved in the use of technology as a quick solution to profound social problems. The problem of heroin addiction has been variously described in moral, social, psychological, legal, and medical terms. The use of methadone involved a decision to define it as a medical problem and to focus on the most manageable and most easily understood of the problems of the addict—his physiological needs. This focus reflects both the assumptions of science—"the art of the soluble"— and the approach of engineering—the systematic application of scientific findings or organized knowledge to specific problems. Problems are subdivided into components. In fact, the most important consequence of technology, according to John Kenneth Galbraith, is "in forcing the division and subdivision of any task into its component parts. Thus, and only thus, can organized knowledge be brought to bear on performance."[3] The aspects of a problem that are selected for solution are those regarded most easily soluble, though they may not necessarily be the most fundamental. As the biologist Peter Medawar remarked, it is the scientist's business to solve problems, not to grapple with them: "The spectacle of a scientist locked in combat with the forces of ignorance is not an inspiring one if, in the outcome, the scientist is routed."[4]

A technological approach requires that a task be precisely defined and the objectives clarified. Once objectives are determined, the relative advantages of alternative solutions can be weighed, and the most appropriate selected. The heroin problem, however, does not permit precise analysis. No one definition of addiction—medical, social, psychological—seems fully satisfactory, and while the task—to free the addict from heroin—is clear, the objectives of methadone maintenance programs are controversial and often vague. Usually these definitions are stated in broad terms of helping the addict to become "a functioning member of society." But, does this goal involve abstinence?

Employment? Is the development of this technique to be considered primarily an economic service to the community and its success to be measured in terms of the money saved in crime and prison costs? Or is it a social service, with emphasis on the well-being of individual patients?

The long and bitter controversy over methadone maintenance reflects these ambiguities. Despite impressive evaluation and the rapid expansion of methadone programs, there has been continuing opposition. To a great extent ambivalence toward methadone maintenance is a reflection of conflicting values within society. Developed at a time of extraordinary public pressure to "solve" the problem of addict-related crimes, methadone maintenance is an attractive solution: it is cost-effective, yielding visible clinical results in providing humane relief to addicted persons. It also meshes well with prevailing assumptions concerning the efficacy of technology, the widespread tendency to regard all problems as amenable to technological solutions.[5] As Margaret Mead has observed, "Right straight through our history we have adopted a policy that invention, technology, ingenuity, resources, ought to be available to deal with anything that we want to have dealt with."[6]

At the same time, the decision to approach the drug problem by seeking a chemical substitute for the addictive drug is based on assumptions that run directly counter to prevailing attitudes about addiction. These are the attitudes of a society that for some fifty years has stigmatized the addict, has regarded his habit as a criminal and virulent form of human deviance, and has handled addiction through punitive legal and social policies. These attitudes are rooted in a tradition that places great value on abstinence, will power, postponement of gratification, and self-control, as well as a strong moral taboo against any drugs that alter moods or weaken individual self-mastery. "Within our religious and moral ethic in the past there has been a tremendous emphasis on self-control, on an individual becoming his own master, being in control of himself through will power, so that any drug that is regarded as addictive . . . comes under reprobation."[7]

The proliferation of methadone programs is a judgment reflecting our growing willingness to ignore the moral stigma of addiction in order to focus on workable remedies. But because there is little systematic knowledge about the etiology of addiction, contradictory and often emotional attitudes persist toward both the problem and the relative advantages of various solutions.

There remain many fundamental disagreements, even among those who work in established methadone programs and seek to expand this approach to the heroin problem. Jerome H. Jaffe, director of the President's Special Action Office for Drug Abuse Prevention, notes disagreement on seven basic issues: whether the goal is to keep patients on medication or to eventually withdraw them, the criteria for determining if maintenance is the most appropriate treatment for an individual, the relative advantages of various opiates and routes of administration, the optimal dosages, the appropriate balance between availability of methadone and the problem of illicit diversion, the contribution of ancillary rehabilitation services to the treatment, and, finally, the social objectives to be reasonably expected of the program.[8]

As a result of such ambiguity methadone programs have developed in a climate of conflict extending from the level of policy down to the actual operation of individual clinics. Addicts themselves are ambivalent about methadone maintenance, viewing it on the one hand as a "last resort," and on the other "as a time to get straight and begin again." Ambivalence is reflected in the fragmented system of regulation and control, in tenuous and erratic funding, and in local community reaction to new programs.

Contributing to the controversy surrounding the methadone program are many difficult ethical, social, and political questions. What is the medical and moral justification for perpetuating an individual's dependence on an addictive drug, for focusing on symptomatic changes in behavior while ignoring the sources of addiction? How do the agencies responsible for regulating and controlling the use of a new medical technology deal with an often vague distinction between treatment and investigative research?

Many of these issues involve questions of power and social control. Therapy, by definition, is context-bound, involving a societal definition of deviance; the goal is to return a situation to a preconceived notion of "normalcy." Sociologists argue that therapy is intended to ensure that "actual or potential deviants stay within the institutionalized confines of reality. . . . Its specific

institutional arrangements . . . from exorcism to psy-
choanalysis, from pastoral care to personnel counseling
programs, belong under the category of social control."[9]
In the case of methadone maintenance, those who
manage the technology have substantial control over the
patient, especially because of the addict's physiological
dependence. Even if men assume such power in the
name of humanitarianism, can responsibility be maintained and abuse be minimized? What role should the
patient have in determining his own treatment?

There are further questions concerning the efficacy of
the technology. An assumption of those who advocate
methadone is that once the patient resolves the physical
problems of addiction, he will be receptive to rehabilitation and able to function "normally." Program organization is necessarily based on the belief that a maintained
addict has a variety of options available to him. But, in
view of the social attitudes toward addiction, will
methadone addicts in fact be accepted even if they are
able to function in society? And what options are
available to those who cannot? Methadone maintenance
has received full support from the federal government,
in particular from the President's Special Action Office
for Drug Abuse Prevention, but what is the reaction at
the local level—the level at which ultimately the
program's goals of rehabilitation must be fulfilled?

This study will first describe social and individual
characteristics of the heroin problem and alternative
solutions. We will then consider the development of
methadone maintenance, first in its larger national
context, and then in the particular social and political

environment of one community, Syracuse, New York. The Syracuse program was selected for study because its day-to-day operation and its many problems clearly illustrate on a microlevel many of the issues that have been raised concerning methadone maintenance. This detailed approach, focusing on the implementation of drug policy in a community, assumes that methadone programs are shaped not only by the effect of the technology itself, but by social and political factors influencing their operation and the lives of their participants. The study, therefore, is not intended as an evaluation of the Syracuse program nor as a judgment of the overall merits of this type of therapy. Rather, it will describe methadone maintenance as a social phenomenon, analyzing the assumptions inherent in the treatment and the implications of the increasing tendency to seek technological solutions to major social problems.

NOTES

[1] Alvin M. Weinberg, "Can Technology Replace Social Engineering?" *University of Chicago Magazine*, 59 (October 1966), 6–7. Note that Amitai Etzioni and Richard Remp, in "Technological 'Short-Cuts' to Social Change," *Science*, 175 (January 7, 1972), 31–38, look at the methadone maintenance program as one of several technological short-cuts which include instructional television, antabuse, the breath analyzer, the intrauterine device, and gun control.

[2] Marie Nyswander, M.D., quoted in Nat Hentoff, *A Doctor among the Addicts* (New York: Grove Press, 1968), p. 53.

[3] John Kenneth Galbraith, *The New Industrial State* (New York: Signet Books, 1967), p. 24.

[4] P.B. Medawar, *The Art of the Soluble* (London: Methuen, 1967), p. 7.

[5]Ironically this is reflected in the increasing use of drugs for mind-altering as well as therapeutic purposes, and 20 percent of all prescriptions sold in the United States are for mind-altering purposes.

[6]Testimony by Margaret Mead in "Competitive Problems of the Drug Industry," *Hearings* before the Subcommittee on Monopoly, Select Committee on Small Business, in U.S. Senate, 91st Congress, 2nd Session, Part 13, October 27, 1969, p. 5458.

[7]*Ibid.*

[8]Jerome H. Jaffe, "Methadone Maintenance and the National Strategy," National Association for the Prevention of Addiction to Narcotics (NAPAN), *Proceedings*, Fourth National Conference on Methadone Treatment, New York, 1972, pp. 37–40.

[9]Peter L. Berger and Thomas Luckman, *The Social Construction of Reality* (New York : Doubleday, 1966), p. 104.

I / The Addict
and Society

The Legislation of Morality[1]

Heroin was synthesized from morphine in 1898. Considered a nonaddictive substitute for morphine, it was used widely as an analgesic and in cough medicines and tonics. Addiction to morphine at this time was regarded as a medical problem, to be treated by physicians. Addiction was not a crime; on the contrary, at the end of the nineteenth century opium addicts were those who would not risk their reputation for temperance by taking alcoholic beverages. According to historians of the period, "They have not come from the ranks of reckless men and fallen women, but the majority of them are to be found among the educated and most honored and useful members of society."[2] Drug addiction at this time was predominantly a problem of women: many of the widely advertised home remedies containing opium as a pain killer were directed to women. But then, in the first decade of the 1900's, addiction sharply increased among members of the "unrespectable" parts of society.[3] From about 1919 to

1923 local city governments supported morphine maintenance clinics in which addicts could receive drugs legally, and there were, according to some estimates, more addicts in the United States then than there are today.[4]

To control an increasing international drug traffic, Congress in 1914 passed the Harrison Act; this imposed a stamp tax on opium products and required suppliers, pharmacists, and physicians to register. More important, however, was an ambiguous clause in the law that exempted physicians from the regulations when they prescribed drugs to a patient in the course of professional practice. In fact, registration was denied to all sellers outside the medical profession. Over the next seven years, a series of Supreme Court decisions influenced by the mood of Prohibition extended the criteria of legitimacy to medical use; doctors could not prescribe drugs to satisfy the "craving" of an addict, but only to aid morphine withdrawal for addicts under institutional care. These rulings, upheld in the conviction of several doctors who gave prescriptions to addicts,[5] led to a new interpretation of addiction that was to dominate medical, legal, and social opinion for nearly fifty years.

Addicts, previously assumed to be physically ill, were now legally defined as criminals. Socially, addicts at best were regarded as "irresponsible, selfish, immature, thrill-seeking individuals who are constantly in trouble—the type of person who acts first and thinks afterward";[6] at worst, they were considered "dope fiends." Gradually "heroin addiction" became a moral category, a "total identity which permeated every situation."[7] Despite substantial evidence that sustained use of heroin may be less debilitating than addiction to barbiturates,[8] society continues to respond more harshly to the heroin addict, stereotyping him as criminal, psychopathic, immoral, and aggressive—a menacing and nonproductive member of society.

For example, after the Harrison Act and the Supreme Court interpretations, doctors were extremely reluctant to treat addicts. Although they could do so legally, they were intimidated by legal harassment and the fear that they would be required to prove in court their good faith and adherence to medical standards.[9] Research as well as medical treatment was curtailed by the policies of the Bureau of Narcotics and by continuing legal harassment. The American Medical Association tried to protect the right of its members to make independent decisions, asserting in a 1924 resolution that

the only proper and scientific method of treating narcotics drugs addicts is under such conditions of control of both the addict and the drug; that any administration of a habit forming drug must be by, or under the direct personal authority, of the physician.[10]

Nevertheless, statements from the American Medical Association reflected the Prohibition mentality underlying government policy. A member of the AMA Committee on Narcotic Drugs wrote in 1921:

The shallow pretense that drug addiction is a disease which the specialist must be allowed to treat, which pretended treatment consists in supplying its victims with the drug which has caused their physical and moral debauchery . . . has been asserted and urged in volumes of literature by self-styled specialists. . . . The vice that causes degeneration of the moral sense, and spreads through social contact, readily infecting the entire community, saps the moral fiber and contaminates the individual members one after another like the rotten apples in a barrel of sound ones. [11]

Until the late 1950's the AMA continued to oppose all ambulatory methods of treating drug addicts despite conflicting opinion within the association. An inevitable result was that addicts, denied medical treatment and legal means to meet the physiological demands of their addiction, turned to criminal activity. Increased police action reduced the supply of heroin and prevented doctors from dispensing it, thereby creating the profitable occupation of "pusher." The cost was driven up along with criminal efforts to obtain heroin. Thus the problem of addiction assumed totally new dimensions.

Enforcement of the Harrison Act was originally the responsibility of the Bureau of Internal Revenue, and then of the Bureau of Prohibition, whose first act was to close the existing government clinics dispensing narcotics. Since 1930 primary responsibility for the control of addiction has rested with the Bureau of Narcotics and Dangerous Drugs (BNDD), a police enforcement agency affiliated with the Department of the Treasury until 1968, and then with the Department of Justice.

With clinics closed and hospitals and private physicians reluctant to risk caring for addicts, the only help routinely available to addicts was the Federal Addiction Treatment Centers set up by the Public Health Service;

one opened in Lexington, Kentucky, in 1935, and the other in Fort Worth, Texas, in 1938. These institutions, created primarily for criminal commitment, have admitted about 89,000 patients; their estimated relapse rate is more than 90 percent,[12] a pattern which has been labeled the "revolving door" syndrome.

By the mid-1950's the public press was reporting a narcotics epidemic. Public and private institutions proposed various remedies. In 1955 a subcommittee of the Senate Judiciary Committee conducted an investigation and concluded that "subversion through drug addiction is an established aim of Communist China" and that the United States is "a principal target." The committee recommended tougher legislation and an increased budget for the Narcotics Bureau. It blasted a proposal for legal distribution of narcotics as "totally unworkable, completely contrary to accepted medical practices and theory," claiming it "would aggravate rather than solve the problems by supplementing the market. . . . Proper law enforcement and confinement in such instances will do much towards minimizing the narcotics traffic in addiction in the United States."[13]

Quite a different response came from a joint committee of the American Bar Association and the AMA. Seeking alternatives to punitive procedures, this committee recommended an experimental facility for outpatient treatment of addicts.[14] But the Narcotics Control Act of 1956 imposed more stringent penalties, and it was not until the 1966 Narcotic Addict Rehabilitation Act that the law recognized that addiction could be treated as a broad social problem rather than as a criminal activity. This act provided federal funds for civil commitment of addicts instead of prosecution for federal offense, and it also provided funds for committing addicts not charged with criminal offense. It included provisions for federal rehabilitation, for posthospital care programs, and for assistance to states and localities to develop their own programs.

In 1966, New York State passed legislation establishing the Narcotics Addiction Control Commission (NACC), charged with prevention of drug abuse, rehabilitating addicts, and doing research on the causes and effects of addiction. The NACC has developed its own program for committing addicts to rehabilitation institutions through criminal or civil procedures.[15] It also provides financial resources for educational and treatment programs in local communities. The NACC has been the major source of support of methadone maintenance as well as of other therapeutic programs, for the burden of funding drug programs has rested almost entirely on the state and local communities. Despite liberalized federal legislation supporting rehabilitation programs, the entire federal budget for drug addiction in 1971 was only $88 million, less than the amount appropriated by the State of New York alone for dealing with its problem.[16]

Defining the Problem

The growing number of addicts and the associated increase in crime have led to a national sense of crisis intensified by the penetration of the problem into middle-class communities. Crisis created confusion, described by one politician as "a situation where the barn is burning and everybody is standing around explaining why they cannot put out the fire, picking a few dandelions off the lawn, but the barn in the meantime is burning down."[17]

There were, according to official estimates from the BNDD, about 515,000 heroin addicts in the United States in March 1972, and an estimated 300,000 in New York City alone.[18] There are several kinds of heroin users. It has been frequently observed that addiction is a young man's problem, that there are few elderly heroin addicts. Death and institutionalization account for some of this depletion, but data suggest that addiction may be a self-limiting process and that about two-thirds of the addicts grow out of heroin addiction by their mid-thirties.[19] Maturation alone seems to enable addicts to give up their habit, but this may follow an expensive and debilitating pattern of life lasting twenty years. Yet there are some people who use opiates only occasionally, and are not addicted. Others are "medical addicts," those addicted inadvertently through the use of morphine in hospital settings. Many physicians and nurses are addicted, but usually they have none of the normal problems of gaining access to drugs. And finally, there are street addicts, the group which society generally identifies as its major social problem.[20]

Increases in the number of street addicts are difficult to assess, for the greater number of *known* addicts in recent years is partly a product of more stringent law enforcement. Yet addiction is an increasingly visible problem. A Gallup Poll indicated that between March 1971 and July 1971, with the publicity concerning veterans' addiction and the possibilities of "contagion," addiction rose from seventh to first place in the public's list of most important social problems.[21] Addiction has generated extraordinary fear, for the high cost of heroin and its illegality means that addicts must commit crimes to support their habit. Furthermore, with greater law enforcement reducing the heroin supply and driving up its cost, addicts become increasingly desperate. The cost of a habit depends on the availability of heroin at any given time and may vary with such unpredictable factors as a dock strike in New York or agricultural conditions in Turkey. For the average user, the cost of a habit ranges from about thirty dollars per day to about sixty dollars per day, and the theft required to support a habit is estimated as high as $55,000 a year.[22] The national financial cost of addiction, including theft and law enforcement, has been estimated by the BNDD at about $3 billion a year, expanding at a rate of about 10 percent annually. Estimates of crime vary, but losses attributed to addicts in New York City alone have ranged as high as $5.5 billion a year. Max Singer, however, has suggested an irony in popular estimates of addict crime, noting that if the problem of crime is approached by asking, "How much property is stolen in New York City, by addicts or anyone else?" the amount attributed to addicts alone is much higher than the total crime estimates.[23] As with most illegal activities, estimates remain extremely crude; the number of addicts and the amount of heroin used are calculated on the basis of the number of persons caught, and to a great extent estimates reflect public attitudes.

Besides crime, the large number of narcotics-related deaths, particularly among young people, has aroused public demands for action.[24] In New York City these increased from 200 in 1960 to over 1,000 in 1970. Nationally, in 1971, 2,000 deaths were attributed to heroin overdoses or diseases caused or exacerbated by drug abuse, such as hepatitis and tuberculosis. Also, many groups and individuals have worried about addicts' difficulties in holding jobs and in caring for their families. And beyond these concerns, which are motivated by fear, economics, and compassion, there are uneasy feelings about drug addiction, for addiction stands as a visible criticism of a society which has not provided a "better solution" for those with social problems.

Responding to social pressure, President Richard M. Nixon in 1971 proposed a $370 million crash program to combat "public enemy No. 1," the national heroin addiction problem, and asked Congress to authorize a Special Action Office for Drug Abuse Prevention. In March 1972 legislation was signed giving this office statutory authority and $200,000 plus control over $800,000 to be spent by the Department of Health, Education, and Welfare. The Special Action Office will have authority to spend $1 billion between 1972 and 1975. President Nixon appointed Dr. Jerome H. Jaffe, who had developed a major rehabilitation program in Illinois, as director of the office, responsible for the coordination of the drug programs of thirteen separate federal agencies. There was considerable disagreement concerning the scope of this office, and whether it should deal exclusively with rehabilitation or with law enforcement as well. The creation of a special drug-abuse law-enforcement office divided these functions, and increased funding was allocated to the control of drug traffic. But the appointment of Jaffe suggests that "the war on drug abuse" involves a commitment to rehabilitation as well, and that "rehabilitation" is defined in therapeutic rather than condemnatory terms.

A pattern for the transition in public policy from punishment to treatment is available in the case of alcoholism. The large-scale "war against alcoholism" in the days of Prohibition failed, and alcoholism has been accepted as a part of Western society despite its high social cost. Thirty thousand automobile deaths a year are attributed to alcohol. An estimated 5 percent of adult Americans at every socioeconomic level have serious drinking problems, and there are 600,000 alcoholics in New York City alone. As in the case of drug addiction, alcoholism is not fully accepted as an illness, but it does not carry the same stigma as drug addiction, and treatment often involves various kinds of sociomedical approaches.[25] Attempts to redefine the problem of drug addiction in sociomedical terms have been much more controversial, and internecine warfare continues among those committed to different approaches to its resolution.

Meaningful preventive or therapeutic measures must be based on an appropriate analysis of the etiology of addiction. Proponents of various measures differ in the relative emphasis they place upon psychological, environmental, or physical factors as the source of addiction.[26] There are those who view addiction as an individual aberration, the consequence of a psychic disorder that demands the satisfaction obtained from drugs. A spokesman for this point of view is Dr. David Ausubel, who talks of "addiction-prone personalities," by nature lethargic and nonproductive: "It is a myth to assume that they can lead normal lives."[27]

Another point of view considers addiction as a rational attempt by individuals to resolve their psychological difficulties and to adapt to a disruptive social or economic environment. Norman Zinberg differentiates "oblivion seekers," who use heroin to escape lives that seem hopeless, from "experience seekers," who by and large use other drugs.[28] For the oblivion seeker, addiction, like other forms of deviance, is a way for him to ignore the gap between societal goals and expectations and the means available to him for reaching them.[29] It is adaptive in that it enables the individual to cope with his frustration; peer group influence is regarded as the key factor in the selection of addiction as an adaptive mechanism.[30]

Many research physicians regard addiction as a metabolic or physiological problem, aggravated by irreversible changes caused by the drug itself. This view is becoming more popular, although research on the subject is still relatively primitive. Because of the long history of legal constraints, few researchers have built their carreers in this field. Furthermore, experimental research on the effects of drugs on human subjects poses obvious difficulties and dangers, so that much of what is known has been found by trial and error or by accidental discovery.[31] Heroin research poses special difficulties. By law morphine rather than heroin must be used for research; this limits empirical knowledge about the differences among the specific effects of morphine, heroin, and methadone.

Much of the recent research on addiction has focused on physiological effects, attempting to find the location and character of biochemical action in the central nervous system, and the extent to which changes are reversible.[32] Narcotics are known to inhibit RNA and protein synthesis and to cause changes in cell membranes, but how such changes occur is unknown, and even the extent to which there is a genuine physical dependence is controversial. The impact of individual needs and motivations on the effect of opiates is difficult to assess.[33] Those who assume a link between physiological and psychological factors seek to determine how pharmacological effects may be conditioned by psychological expectations. For example, the work of Maurice H. Severs indicates that drug-seeking behavior is based on psychological conditioning which is only later reinforced by actual physical effects.[34] Some researchers are investigating genetic factors leading to addiction-prone behavior.[35]

Proposed Solutions

The variety of attempts to deal with addiction reflect the disagreement about its character. Those who see the

source of addiction as primarily a psychological problem
focus on the susceptible individual and are generally
committed to abstinence programs. Some feel that
punitive repressive measures may be the only solution,
while others look to therapeutic communities. Except
for the projects of a few political groups, and attempts at
preventive education, drug programs devote little
attention to factors in the community that may lead an
individual to addiction. The predominant mode of
rehabilitation focuses on the physical aspects of addiction. Methadone maintenance programs and current
research to find drugs that will act as heroin antagonists
by physically blocking its euphoric effect focus on the
agent itself; the emphasis is on the addict's social
adjustment regardless of abstinence per se. The
relationship of rehabilitation measures to assumptions
about the etiology of addiction is summarized in Table 1.

Treatment programs reflecting all three approaches
proliferate, provoking one writer to remark, "Drug
treatment programs are the most popular hustle . . .
since poverty programs passed from vogue a few years
ago."[36]

The key word in this hustle is "multimodality," an
expression coined by Dr. Jaffe, which refers to a concept
of rehabilitation that coordinates within a single
administrative structure all varieties of approaches to
addiction. He explains that the advantage to this
approach is that "program planning and expansion can
then be based on the results of a fair and uniform
evaluation system imposed by the administrative structure, rather than by emotion, rhetoric, and political trial

Table 1.   Approaches to rehabilitation°

Assumptions about the cause of addiction	Focus of rehabilitation	Rehabilitation approach
psychological factors	susceptible individual	abstinence programs, therapeutic communities, punishment
environmental factors	the community	education, employment, housing, etc. political change
physical factors	the addiction	methadone or heroin maintenance, narcotics antagonists

°This model is adapted from Ross A. McFarland, "The Epidemiology of Motor Vehicle Accidents," *Journal of the American Medical Association*, 180 (April 1962), 103–114.

at arms in the lists of the mass media."[37] In fact, however, programs using different treatment approaches often compete rather than complement each other: the relationship among existing drug programs thus mirrors the conflicting attitudes toward definitions of drug abuse held by the professional world and by society at large.

Approaches to addiction have fostered several types of rehabilitation programs: medical detoxification clinics, self-help therapeutic communities, political and religious movements, and pharmacological efforts.

Detoxification clinics ease the physical difficulty of heroin withdrawal by giving diminishing doses of methadone over a period of one to three weeks to alleviate withdrawal symptoms. There are both inpatient and outpatient detoxification programs—and each approach has strong advocates.[38] In some cases detoxification programs include counseling and assistance in finding employment or training. Patients are often referred to self-help programs such as Synanon, for without continuing rehabilitation the relapse rate is high.

There are a variety of self-help community programs; some are residence units, others are day-care centers offering psychiatric therapy, counseling, and social services. They usually require that the addict commit himself totally to the program and completely abstain from all drugs. He confronts his problems with the help of others in the therapeutic community; once rehabilitated himself, he is expected to remain a participant in the program. Former addicts remain as counselors or at least continue to participate in the social activities of the community.

Many of these programs are run by former addicts whose objective is to assist the addict in meeting his own emotional needs and in developing constructive behavioral patterns. Live-in communities such as Synanon and Daytop Village in New York attempt to "convert" the individual, often through brutal confrontations in which he is forced by group pressure to face his own problems.[39] This approach tends to be puritanical: self-control and the obligations of the individual to the group are emphasized. Advocates of these methods express a messianic faith in their effectiveness. Success is defined in terms of total abstinence and the intensity of the residents' commitment to the program's objectives. While the nature of the treatment limits the number of individuals who can be involved, the success rate of those who remain is considered by proponents of the method to be high.[40] Nonresident centers tend to operate with a similar approach, focusing on the individual's personal adjustment to the new social group that forms around the treatment program.

Other groups are working on drug problems, but as a secondary focus. Some religious groups have required a drug-free life as a condition for participation, for example the Black Muslims. Evangelical organizations such as the Teen Challenge Center attempt to rehabilitate through religious conversion. "Transcendental meditation" has been proposed as a treatment; an experiment involving 1,862 subjects using soft drugs indicated that this easily learned mental technique is an effective means of decreasing drug abuse.[41] Some organizations with political goals function as therapeutic communities. The Black Man's Development Center of Washington, D.C., for example, has dual goals of addiction treatment and building a "solid bond of black brotherhood." Other political organizations, such as the Young Lords in New York, are taking an increasingly active role in controlling drug pushers and in encouraging abstinence. In some neighborhoods, gangs and vigilante groups opposed to the use of drugs are forming to keep out pushers. These multipurpose organizations are the only ones that actively seek to modify the environment.

Many addicts fail to respond to the confrontation tactics of therapeutic communities, and for these, a pharmacological solution such as methadone is becoming popular as the most promising alternative. These drugs relieve the physical symptoms and demands of heroin so that the addict can lead a fairly normal life. A model exists in the system used in Great Britain and in Scandinavia, where an addict may obtain heroin from government-operated centers and by prescription from physicians. A basic assumption in this approach is that narcotics addiction is a medical problem, and that drug craving is based on physiological need. The hard core addict, it is assumed, continues using heroin not so much for its euphoric effects as to avoid the discomfort of withdrawal.[42] Advocates of methadone maintenance emphasize its medicinal role, in part as a conciliatory gesture to public antipathy toward addiction. They compare methadone for addicts to insulin for diabetics, and do not consider avoiding addiction per se important. Nor is the treatment concerned with the source of addiction; its major goal is to resolve the one aspect of the problem that appears to be manageable, that is, to relieve the addict of the necessity for continuous hustling. Vincent Dole, one of the doctors responsible for developing the program, explained his point of view: "It does not strike me as relevant whether these patients ever get off methadone. Some may want to and that's fine. But what is relevant is that a treatment can be developed so that the addict can become a socially useful citizen, happy in himself and in society. That's much more important than whether he's on or off a medication."[43] And a more distant but related goal is to destroy the market for heroin by providing an effective and legal substitute.

The highly controversial nature of this philosophy was evident in the explosive response to a 1971 proposal to stabilize addicts by dispensing control doses of heroin for up to six months.[44] The purpose was to motivate young addicts to participate in other rehabilitation programs. The proposed program, not surprisingly, proved to be politically unviable. In February 1972, however, a Manhattan assemblyman, Antonio Olivieri, sponsored a bill to open heroin-dispensing clinics as a "holding pattern" to get addicts off the streets so that they would not have to commit crimes. By this time, the proposal received some qualified support as a last resort, in particular from New York City Police Commissioner Patrick V. Murphy. Many oppose the opening of such clinics, however, on the grounds that heroin would be diverted to the black market. Although methadone is a narcotic similar to heroin, fewer objections to its use have been raised, and it has become the most well-known and widely accepted pharmacological agent used to control opiate addiction. This success is due in part to the fact that its proponents have been careful to emphasize its medicinal role.

Research continues on other chemical agents for therapeutic use: one is dl alpha-acetylmethadol, sometimes called "laam," which needs to be administered only three times a week. Some researchers are developing and testing narcotics antagonists, such as cyclazocine and naloxone, both of which block the euphoric effects of morphine.[45] Administered after detoxification from heroin, these agents deter readdiction with relatively few morphinelike side effects. Although to be effective they must be administered daily, the antagonists are not regarded as narcotics—that is, they produce neither euphoria nor addictive dependence. But little is known about the long-term effects of their daily use, and the amount of research has been minimal, for it is not a potentially profitable area for private pharmaceutical companies.[46] In view of the industry's reluctance to make a firm research commitment to this area, in 1971 the U.S. House of Representatives Select Committee on Crime called for a commitment "with the same priority as the Manhattan Project," proposing a $50 million national research program to develop a drug to cure heroin addiction.

Despite a growing number of rehabilitation programs, it has been estimated that only 20 percent to 40 percent of addicts voluntarily seek treatment.[47] For society, alternatives to treatment are costly. Imprisonment of an addict costs about $8,000 per year, and the relapse rate after release is virtually 100 percent. Alternatively, there are National Institute of Mental Health (NIMH) centers, such as Lexington, and several other institutions at the state level that admit both voluntary patients and patients referred by the courts. These are estimated to cost about thirty dollars per day per patient, and, with few provisions for follow-up services, they too have high relapse rates.[48] Residential therapeutic communities cost about twelve dollars per patient per day.[49] Methadone programs require fewer facilities, less capital outlay, and fewer experienced personnel than many other types of treatment programs. The cost of administering methadone in a clinic is about five dollars per person per day, or $2,000 a year (see Table 2).[50]

Table 2.   Estimated relative costs of drug programs, per addict per year

NIMH civil commitment	$10,000–$12,000	
Prison	$ 8,000	
Therapeutic communities	$ 4,400	(plus welfare)
Methadone maintenance	$ 2,000	(plus welfare)

Besides its relatively low cost, methadone treatment has become popular for other reasons. In an emergency, the public demands immediate solutions; new techniques are often embraced with enthusiasm.[51] They appeal as a potential panacea, as a means to "wipe out" a problem. The rapid expansion of the methadone program reflects this predisposition, as well as a public approach to problems that "declares war"—on poverty, on crime, on pollution, or on addiction. Jaffe has discussed adapting techniques used in Vietnam to the civilian problem, requiring urinalysis tests in schools and other institutions to identify early heroin users, and forcing them to submit to detention and treatment.[52] Moreover, in the light of the striking success of medicine in dealing with disease, redefining a social problem in medical terms provides a comforting and promising approach, placing a complex, ill-defined problem in a well-defined context. Thus, despite

continuing medical, legal, and moral opposition, methadone maintenance is widely regarded as a major
breakthrough in the treatment of drug addiction.

NOTES

[1]Troy Duster, in *The Legislation of Morality* (New York: The Free Press, 1969), discusses the relationship of law to morality as suggested by the history of the narcotics problem. Through a sociological analysis of the impact of changing legislation, he suggests "how the law can shift neutral behavior into that which is strongly overladen with moral condemnation." p. 27.

[2]Charles E. Terry and Mildred Pellens, *The Opium Problem* (New York: Committee on Drug Addiction and Bureau of Social Hygiene, 1928), (Reprinted New York: Patterson, 1970). For a social history of addiction, see David Musto, *Narcotics and America: A Social History* (New Haven: Yale University Press, 1972).

[3]See Duster, *op. cit.*, p. 11, for an analysis of the relationship between social class factors and changing legislation.

[4]Estimates of the number of addicts at that time range from 215,000 to 1,000,000. Rufus King, in "Narcotic Drug Laws and Enforcement Policies," *Law and Contemporary Problems*, 22 (Winter 1957), 120, discusses the sources of these varying estimates.

[5]For a discussion of the Supreme Court decisions following the Harrison Act and their implications, see Alfred R. Lindesmith, *The Addict and the Law* (Bloomington: Indiana University Press, 1965), p. 15.

[6]Quoted from a 1951 pamphlet put out by the U.S. Public Health Service in Duster, *op. cit.*, p. 20.

[7]*Ibid.*, p. 68.

[8]Donald Louria, *Overcoming Drugs* (New York: McGraw-Hill, 1971), p. 98.

[9]Lindesmith, *op. cit.*, pp. 257–262.

[10]Text of report cited in King, *op. cit.*, p. 124.

[11]Quoted in Lindesmith, *op. cit.*, p. 146.

[12]Nathan B. Eddy, M.D., "Current Trends in the Treatment of Drug Dependence and Drug Abuse," *Bulletin on Narcotics*, 22, (January–March 1970), 1–9.

[13]These quotations are excerpts from U.S. Senate, Judiciary Committee, *Hearings before the Subcommittee on Improvements in the Federal Criminal Code*, 84th Congress, 1st Session, June 1955, pp. 2–4.

[14]Joint Committee of the ABA/AMA on Narcotic Drugs, *Drug Addiction-*
—Crime or Disease, Interim and Final Report (Bloomington: Indiana
University Press, 1961).

[15]See "The New Narcotic Addiction Control Act—New York Mental
Hygiene Law, Article 9," *Albany Law Review*, 31 (1967), 336–344.

[16]See U.S. House of Representatives, Select Committee on Crime,
Hearings, 92nd Congress, 1st Session, Part 2, p. 572, for a discussion of the
imbalance.

[17]Representative Sam Steiger, Republican, Arizona, *ibid.*, p. 462.

[18]Reported in *Wall Street Journal*, July 27, 1972.

[19]Donald Louria, *The Drug Scene* (New York: McGraw-Hill, 1968), pp.
177–178, and Charles Winick, "The Life Cycle of the Narcotics Addict and of
Addiction," *Bulletin on Narcotics*, 16 (January–March 1964), 1–11. Whether
the decline in drug use is the result of a decrease in need, an increase in
resistance, or some combination of factors, is unknown.

[20]There is a literature differentiating the various types of narcotics users.
This is reviewed in Paul Roman and Harrison Trice, *Spirits and Demons at
Work: Alcohol and Other Drugs on the Job* (Ithaca: New York State Industrial
and Labor Relations, Cornell University, 1972), Chapter 3. See also Charles
Winick, "Physician Narcotics Addicts," in Howard S. Becker, ed., *The Other
Side: Perspectives on Deviants* (Glencoe, Ill.: The Free Press, 1964), pp.
261–279.

[21]See "National Affairs," *Newsweek*, July 5, 1971, p. 28. A widely
disseminated report estimated that 15 percent of the men in Vietnam are
hooked on heroin, which is available there in high-grade form (*Life*, July 23,
1971). The dynamics of "contagion" is analyzed in Richard D. Alarcon, M.D.,
"Spread of Heroin Abuse in the Community," *Bulletin on Narcotics*, 21
(July–September 1969), 17–22.

[22]The economics of heroin addiction and the effect of law enforcement on
its market price is analyzed in Mark Moore, "Economics of Heroin
Addiction," John F. Kennedy School of Government, Harvard University,
Report 4, 1971 (mimeographed).

[23]Max Singer, "The Vitality of Mythical Numbers," *Public Interest*, (Spring
1971) pp. 3–9. See also M. Cronin, "An Analysis of Alternate Heroin Addicts
Treatment Programs" (mimeographed, March 1971). Also, Health Policy
Advisory Center, *Bulletin*, June 1970, claims that crime statistics related to
addicts are grossly exaggerated, and that only about 10 percent of major
felony property crimes are actually committed by addicts. There is a similar
tendency to attribute the problems of the welfare system to the cost of
addiction. According to the Human Resources Administration in New York
City, the 32,000 welfare addicts are threatening to "paralyze" the welfare
system (*New York Times*, March 16, 1972).

[24]Narcotics-related deaths are reported to be the largest single cause of

death for those between fifteen and thirty-five (*New York Times*, March 21, 1972).

[25]See W.G. Dewhirst, "Drug Dependence: An Analysis," *Alberta Law Review*, 9 (1971), 215–249, and H.P. Chalfant and Richard Kurtz, "Alcoholism and the Sick Role," *Journal of Health and Social Behavior*, 12 (March 1971), 66–72.

[26]Note the similarities to the conflicting interpretations of mental illness and the appropriate cures discussed in Anselm Strauss *et al.*, *Psychiatric Ideologies and Institutions* (Glencoe, Ill.: The Free Press, 1964).

[27]David Ausubel, M.D., *Why Compulsory Closed Ward Treatment*. N.Y. State NACC Reprint, No. 5 (1968), p. 4.

[28]Norman F. Zinberg, "Facts and Fallacies about Drug Addiction," *Public Interest*, 6 (Winter 1967), 75–90.

[29]See Robert K. Merton, *Social Theory and Social Structure* (Glencoe, Ill.: The Free Press, 1957), for a discussion of anomie.

[30]Jordan Scher, M.D., *Patterns and Profiles of Addiction and Drug Abuse*, N.Y. State NACC Reprint, 1969, and Harvey W. Feldman, "Ideological Support to Becoming and Remaining a Heroin Addict," *Drug Dependence* (NIMH), 3 (March 1970), 3–11.

[31]See Bernard Barber, *Drugs and Society* (New York: Russell Sage Foundation, 1967), Chapter 2: "Discovery and Testing Processes," pp. 6–38. Rene Dubos, "On the Present Limitations of Drug Research," in Paul Taladay, ed., *Drugs in Our Society* (Baltimore: Johns Hopkins Press, 1964), p. 37.

[32]See for example A.P. Amarose *et al.*, "Chromosomal Analysis of Bone Marrow and Peripheral Blood in Subjects with a History of Illicit Drug Use," *Archives of General Psychiatry*, 25 (August 1971), 181–186, and W.D. Noteboom and G.C. Mueller, "Inhibition of Cell Growth and the Synthesis of Ribonucleic Acid and Protein in Hela Cells by Morphinans and Related Compounds," *Molecular Pharmacology*, 5 (January 1969), 38–48. A summary of such research appears in "Exploring the Nature of Heroin Addiction," *Medical World News*, September 10, 1970, pp. 57ff.

[33]Isidor Chein, *The Road to H* (New York: Basic Books, 1964), p. 359.

[34]See *Medical World News*, September 10, 1970, p. 66.

[35]See for example R. Eriksson *et al.*, "Genetic Analysis of Susceptibility to Morphine Addiction in Inbred Mice," *Annales Medicinae Experimentalis et Biologiae Fenniae*, 49 (1971), 73–78, and J.R. Nichols, "Morphine as a Reinforcing Agent: Laboratory Studies of Its Capacity to Change Behavior," *Research Publications of the Association for Research in Nervous and Mental Disease*, 46, No. 23 (1968), 299–310.

[36]Editorial in Health Policy Advisory Committee *Bulletin*, June 1970, p. 9.

[37]Jerome Jaffe, M.D., in U.S. House of Representatives, Select Committee on Crime, *Hearings*, 92nd Congress, 1st Session, Part 1, April

1971, 211. Prior to his appointment, Jaffe was director of the drug-abuse program of the Illinois State Department of Mental Health, where he established a major multimodality program.

[38]For a review of the literature, see Carl D. Chambers, Ph.D., Walter R. Cuskey, Ph.D., and William F. Wieland, M.D., "Predictors of Attrition during the Outpatient Detoxification of Opiate Addicts," *Bulletin on Narcotics*, 22 (October–December 1970), 43–48.

[39]Louis Yablonsky, *The Tunnel Back: Synanon* (New York: MacMillan, 1965), pp. 263–266.

[40]See discussions of the success of various programs in Judith Calof, *A Study of Four Voluntary Treatment and Rehabilitation Programs for New York City's Narcotic Addicts* (New York: Community Service Society of New York, 1967), and M. Cronin, "An Analysis of Alternative Heroin Addiction Treatment Programs" (draft copy, mimeographed, Washington, D.C., March 1971).

[41]Herbert Benson, "Yoga for Drug Abuse," *New England Journal of Medicine*, 281 (1969), 1133.

[42]Depending on the size of their habit, addicts usually experience the first withdrawal symptoms in the form of anxiety within a few hours after a fix. Physical symptoms, resembling the symptoms of a very bad case of flu, occur in about twelve hours, reaching full intensity in twenty-four to forty-eight hours. See Charles T. Brown, "Morphine Withdrawal," *U.S. Armed Forces Medical Journal*, 1, No. 3 (March 1950), and Alfred R. Lindesmith, *Addiction and Opiates* (Chicago: Aldine, 1968), pp. 28–34.

[43]Vincent Dole, M.D., quoted in Nat Hentoff, *A Doctor among the Addicts* (New York: Grove Press, Evergreen Black Cat ed. 1970), p. 117.

[44]This proposal prepared by the Vera Institute of Justice is similar to the British practice in that heroin is used to stabilize addicts and addiction is regarded as a medical problem. But in England, addicts are maintained on maintenance doses of heroin over long periods of time. Moreover, in the British system, a physician may provide prescriptions in areas where clinics do not dispense drugs.

[45]See Nathan B. Eddy, M.D., "Current Trends in the Treatment of Drug Dependence and Drug Abuse," *Bulletin on Narcotics*, 22 (January–March 1970) 1–9. See also Allen L. Hammond, "Narcotics Antagonists: New Methods to Treat Heroin Addicts," *Science*, August 17, 1971, 503–506.

[46]Statement by Robert L. DuPont, M.D., director, Washington, D.C., Narcotics Treatment Administration in U.S. House of Representatives, Committee on Crime on Narcotics Research, Rehabilitation and Treatment, *Hearings*, 92nd Congress, 1st Session, April, 1971, pp. 143ff.

[47]Louria, *op. cit.*, p. 180.

[48]Bernard Langenauer, M.D., "A Follow-up Study of Narcotics Addicts in the NARA Program," *American Journal of Psychiatry*, 128 (July 1971), 73–77.

[49]See Cronin, *op. cit.*, and Calof, *op. cit.*, for estimated costs of various kinds of rehabilitation treatments.

[50]Cronin, *op. cit.* Methadone cost varies depending on the extent of services. The Medicaid rate for New York City was $9.25 per visit in November 1971.

[51]Joseph Eaton, in *Stone Walls Not a Prison Make* (Springfield: Charles C. Thomas, 1962), p. 32, calls this tendency "newism." He describes how new techniques of treatment, even before they are tested, tend to replace older techniques, and are adopted with an uncritical enthusiasm almost as a social movement.

[52]*New York Times*, April 12, 1972.

II / *Methadone Maintenance*

The Technology[1]

Methadone maintenance is a procedure through which an addict is provided with daily oral doses of methadone usually in a closely-controlled clinic setting. The addict receives an increasing amount of methadone until he reaches a dose regarded by the physician as stabilizing, that is, sufficient to provide a cross-tolerance effect which will block the euphoric effects of heroin should the addict try to return to his former habit. This dose may vary from 30 to 120 milligrams per day. Once the addict is brought up to the desired level, he receives this amount daily for an indefinite period of time. As long as he is on methadone, he will not feel the "rush" or euphoria from heroin, and thus the reward of a "fix" is removed. The actual effectiveness of this technique varies considerably among individual patients. It is usually explained in terms of its physiological impact in reducing drug hunger. But some researchers, noting how little is known about the chemical basis of addiction, prefer to explain methadone in terms of conditioning; by abolishing the pleasurable effect of heroin, it weakens the conditioned behavior pattern that drives the addict

37

to continued use of heroin.[2] However, methadone does not dull depression or anxiety as does heroin, nor when taken orally does it provide the satisfaction that derives from the ritual of "mainlining" (although when mainlined it has similar euphoric effects). Thus it can facilitate behavior change only for an addict who is highly motivated to discontinue the use of heroin.

Using methadone to maintain an addict is, for several reasons, a more satisfactory treatment than the heroin maintenance system which has been used in Great Britain. Unlike heroin, methadone is absorbed effectively through the gastrointestinal tract and is effective for a full twenty-four hours. It is, therefore, administered orally only once a day. There also appear to be fewer "ups and downs" with methadone than with heroin; the addict does not require increasingly larger doses to remain comfortable. Methadone withdrawal symptoms develop more slowly and last longer than heroin withdrawal symptoms, but they are less intense. However, the possibility of complete withdrawal remains uncertain. One study claims that withdrawal from methadone addiction is harmless, with little danger of severe physical reaction.[3] But programs have had only limited success in attempting to withdraw patients stabilized on methadone. For example, Vincent Dole withdrew methadone from 350 patients to find that their heroin hunger returned. And others have reported some success with highly motivated addicts if withdrawal is eased with decreasing amounts of methadone and continuing interpersonal support.[4]

As far as is known, opiates, including both methadone

and heroin, if taken in controlled doses, cause few physiologically debilitating side effects, though there are individual differences in the reaction to all drugs. It is also sometimes difficult to distinguish new discomforts from those due to the earlier use of heroin under unsanitary and irregular conditions. Experience to date suggests, however, that there are no immediate toxic effects of methadone on liver or kidneys, nor impairment of motor functions; the most evident problems are a mild perspiring and constipation. But the long-term physiological impact of extended methadone treatment remains unknown, and there is only limited scientific understanding of its effects on the performance and behavior of patients.

A degree of risk is inevitably involved in the methadone maintenance programs. "Normal" methadone doses are lethal for nonaddicts, and there are frequent reports of fatal poisonings of children who accidentally take their parents' methadone premixed with fruit juice. There have also been overdose deaths among adults who come to a clinic unaddicted and without the tolerance built up from previous narcotics addiction, for the techniques to diagnose the extent of addiction and the level of individual tolerance are inadequate. The effect on the infants of methadone-dependent mothers is also controversial. Some researchers report no evidence of withdrawal syndrome in these infants,[5] but a committee from the American Academy of Pediatrics observed infants with methadone withdrawal symptoms and noted that these were more difficult to control than the symptoms of the heroin-addicted infant. And observations of fifty babies born to methadone mothers in 1971 reported thirty-five with symptoms of withdrawal ranging from unusual irritability to convulsions. [6]

The legality of methadone is its major advantage over heroin. The most serious physiological problems faced by heroin users are due to the irregular availability and poor quality of the drug. The unsanitary conditions of "mainlining" heroin cause diseases such as hepatitis. The acceptability of methadone and its administration in the regulated setting of a medical clinic in which potency and quality are controlled minimizes dangers of disease and overdose. Legalized distribution of heroin in medical clinics would have this same advantage, and some propose this practice to meet the needs of addicts unwilling to accept methadone treatment.

Methadone is not a new drug; it was developed during World War II by the German chemical cartel I.G. Farben as a synthetic pain-killer. After the war, the Technical Industrial Intelligence Committee of the United States Department of State studied the existing research on methadone, and the drug was subsequently marketed in the States as an analgesic under the trade names of Dolophine (after Adolph Hitler), Adanon, Amidone, and Althose. It has been used illegally as a street narcotic, often called a "dolly," but it is available only in small quantities because of difficulties of manufacture. Only two clandestine laboratories have been uncovered in twenty years, one in 1952, the other in 1969. Most street methadone, therefore, is of legal manufacture, obtained through loose prescription practices.

Methadone has been prescribed since 1948 to facilitate the detoxification of heroin addicts. But only since 1963 has methadone been used for the maintenance treatment of heroin addiction. The effectiveness of methadone as a maintenance narcotic was discovered accidentally. Marie Nyswander, M.D., a psychiatrist, and Vincent Dole, M.D., an internist, both from the Rockefeller Institute and Beth-Israel Medical Center, were looking for ways to relieve drug craving. In October 1963 they prescribed large amounts of methadone to two patients who had been taking such high doses of heroin that they were continually drowsy. The methadone was provided to reduce their heroin need, but striking changes in the behavior of the patients led to further exploration of this procedure through a series of planned investigations.

In New York State there had been no extensive research in this area until, in February 1962, the Medical Society of the County of New York ruled that physicians who participate in a properly controlled and supervised clinical research project for addicts on a noninstitutional basis would be deemed to be practicing ethical medicine."[7] This was the first action of its kind to be taken by an official medical society since the Harrison Act. The ruling made possible systematic clinical investigation of the use of methadone, and a program involving six patients began in January 1964 at Rockefeller University.

By March 1965, Doctors Dole and Nyswander had the use of four rooms in the Morris J. Bernstein Institute of the Beth-Israel Medical Center, and they began to admit patients. Two years later there were 350 addicts in the program and many on a waiting list. By October 1969 the number of patients in the Bernstein Institute increased to 719, and dispensing clinics had been set up throughout the New York City area with a total of 1,744 patients. As of March 31, 1971, the program had expanded to include eighty-two ambulatory (outpatient) facilities and thirteen inpatient facilities in New York City and Westchester County, with 7,000 patients and an admission rate of about 700 patients per month.[8] And, by March 1972 it was estimated that 65,000 addicts throughout the country were maintained on methadone.

While most programs are in major cities, such as New York, Washington, D.C., Chicago, and Boston, many small cities such as Syracuse, N.Y., are routinely seeking funds for methadone maintenance programs as a primary means of handling their drug abuse problems.

Program Variations

Methadone programs vary considerably despite standardization required by federal guidelines. Some of this variation represents deliberate experimentation or policy differences, but much of it also reflects tight budgets, local exigencies, and conflicting opinions, even among those who support pharmacological modes of addiction treatment. The first program at the Bernstein Institute provided several models. The initial Beth-Israel plan called for six weeks' hospitalization until a maintenance dosage was established. This was followed by an outpatient phase lasting about a year, during which patients reported daily for medication, urine testing, and intensive services such as group therapy and vocational counseling. Gradually patients came at less frequent intervals, taking their medication home. A third phase required minimal patient contact with the clinic except for weekly visits to pick up a methadone supply.

As the program grew, the inpatient phase was dropped except for patients with medical or psychiatric complications. Outpatient units were decentralized; clinics are now held in storefronts and churches in local neighborhoods, each handling no more than 150 patients. And to keep up with increasing applications within a limited budget, new units have been added in which methadone alone is provided without ancillary counseling services. A city-run program started by Mayor John Lindsay has adopted an elaborate computerized program-planning model to resolve problems of coordination and yet maintain diversification. Patients are screened to determine the level of service appropriate to their needs.[9]

Despite widespread agreement on the importance of a multimodal approach for most patients, budgetary difficulties in many communities have been a major constraint on diversification, forcing new programs to forego the inpatient phase, to shorten the period of intense supervision, and to cut down on ancillary services. A survey of forty-seven programs[10] found group psychotherapy available in thirty-six, vocational rehabilitation in twenty, and recreational programs in eight. Eight programs combine methadone with a residential therapeutic community, and a New Haven group is experimenting with a system in which methadone patients must participate in three hours of group therapy daily.[11] In Boston, however, a clinic funded at $150,000 a year serving 450 patients is so overcrowded that it can offer nothing but methadone.[12] Larger programs, located in cities where the heroin problems are most severe, have long waiting lists[13] and a growing sense of urgency. Their approach is pragmatic; to bring to as many addicts as possible at least the minimum benefits of methadone, and where resources permit, to help patients with their immediate needs such as employment, training, and housing.

Just as programs vary their services, so do they vary the amount of methadone they give to patients. Low-dose programs provide from 20 to 40 milligrams per day; a high dose may be as large as 180 milligrams. Those who favor high doses argue that a safe margin is necessary to establish cross-tolerance. Without this effect, they feel that patients will use the program only to reduce and not to remove their heroin need. For example, a doctor in New York operated a clinic that supplied 3,500 patients with only 40 milligrams of methadone each. Patients continued to use heroin, and the clinic eventually lost its certification. Yet, in Chicago, Jerome Jaffe experimented successfully with doses of 50 to 60 milligrams, on the assumption that many patients merely require relief of the symptom of narcotics hunger.[14] And in a program in Philadelphia, the effects of both high and low doses were observed to be similar. Patients on lower doses had a slightly better employment record, though a greater incidence of continued use of heroin. Patients in both groups, however, continued to use amphetamines and barbiturates.[15] The effect of differing doses of methadone on drug craving remains uncertain because of the limited understanding of the sources of addiction. The high incidence of "cheating" suggests that, at least for some, drug craving continues and that motivation of individual patients appears to be an important consideration.

Some programs use a standardized dose for all patients; others vary doses according to the individual response. In most programs, the dosage is "blind," that is, the patient does not know the amount of methadone he is taking. A "double-blind" procedure, in which neither the physician nor the patient knows the amount of methadone, is also used in some programs. These procedures are intended to prevent the patients' manipulation of physicians and to provide better understanding of the association between dosage and side effects. In the Beth-Israel program, however, patients are told their dosage, and requests for change are often respected. Differences in dosage tend to be associated with variation in program objectives. Programs giving low doses usually have eventual narcotics abstinence as a goal while high-dose programs assume prolonged maintenance.[16]

Variations in program objectives also account for

different admission requirements. The NIMH recommends a minimum age of twenty-one years and at least two documented attempts at abstinence prior to admission. But as methadone programs face increasing pressure to supply at least minimum service to large numbers, there is a tendency to loosen the requirements. For example, the Beth-Israel program has reduced the minimum age for beginning treatment from twenty years to eighteen years, and the number of addiction years from five to two. Some programs continue to exclude mixed drug users and those with medical complications, but most are relaxing such requirements. Several programs work with adolescents, providing maintenance doses of methadone as a means of getting them involved in other kinds of rehabilitation.[17]

Methadone programs also vary in their degree of leniency. All programs require periodic urine testing to indicate whether patients have continued to use heroin. In strict programs, a urine positive that indicates continued use of narcotics is grounds for suspension; the urine test is essentially a means of control. Lenient programs use this test primarily as a means of program evaluation and consider suspension only if a patient is distributing clinic methadone illegally. In those cities where addiction has become a major criminal problem, clinics are reluctant to suspend patients, for the results are dismal. One study of sixty-six suspended patients documented their subsequent record of arrest and hospitalization, and concluded that stringent clinic regulations would only turn more people to the streets, exacerbating the social problem.[18]

Programs also differ in the extent to which patients are involved in establishing policy and selecting new staff members. A California program has a patients' council helping to form program policy through democratic procedures.[19] Many programs feel that the staff should include former addicts sensitive to the anxieties of new patients, who can help to develop their trust in the program. The survey of forty-seven programs cited above found that twenty-seven employed former addicts as assistants.

Legal and Administrative Controls[20]

Despite considerable variation, all programs operate within an elaborate system of federal and state regulation.

Prospective sponsors of a methadone clinic face a bureaucratic jungle. Complex federal and state regulations reflect several governmental concerns: to control the possibilities of abuse inherent in the use of an addictive drug, to safeguard human welfare through regulating the use of new drugs, to supervise the activities of medical care institutions, and to administer government-financed programs. Implementing each concern requires a set of bureaucratic procedures.

Federal Procedures

To open a program one must first register with the Bureau of Narcotics and Dangerous Drugs (BNDD) of the Department of Justice. This agency, in cooperation with the Secretary of the Department of Health,

Education, and Welfare (HEW) reviews the qualifications of applicants, the merits of the research protocol, and the adequacy of the safeguards against illicit diversion of methadone.[21] In addition, under the Control Substance Act of 1970, the applicant must register with the Attorney General in order to purchase the drug.[22]

The BNDD is charged with prevention of drug abuse and control of criminal activity. Its regulations make no provision for research and, until 1970, the bureau's official position was that methadone maintenance programs were illegal under the Harrison Act. In 1970, guided by a cautious statement of approval by a joint committee from the American Medical Association and National Research Council, the BNDD tentatively announced that "the data which has thus far been collected suggests that the drug used in the proper fashion may offer some promises in the treatment and rehabilitation of certain narcotics addicts." It added, however, that merely to "supply addicts with methadone without supplying the necessary therapeutic services and controls is not apt to improve their condition, deter criminal activity or benefit society."[23] Though the BNDD reluctantly recognizes methadone maintenance programs, its central concern remains control of the illegal diversion of methadone.

Federal registration procedures also require application to the Food and Drug Administration (FDA), which, under the 1962 Amendment of the Federal Food, Drug and Cosmetic Act, must approve new drug applications to ensure their safety and efficacy.[24] For while methadone has long been approved as an analgesic, as an ingredient in cough medicine, and as a means to treat withdrawal symptoms, its new use required reevaluation of the drug by the FDA. The FDA ruled that when methadone is used as a maintenance narcotic, it is officially categorized as an Investigative New Drug (IND), a status which limits its use solely to qualified experts for research purposes. New programs must apply for an IND number to the FDA before they can purchase methadone. By the end of 1971 the FDA had assigned 298 numbers to sponsors representing 380 programs, and, with applications continuing to arrive, the distinction between treatment and investigation rapidly was becoming extremely ambiguous, and continued IND status increasingly controversial.[25]

Some methadone advocates claimed that IND status obstructed their attempts to expand their programs. One private physician attempting to cooperate with a licensed methadone program described his experience as including "a police investigation, a threat to my license to practice medicine, and a shower of verbal abuse from representatives of the FDA, the BNDD, and the State Department of Licensing and Regulation who questioned my professional competence and ethics in an unbelievably authoritarian and arbitrary manner."[26] Vincent Dole, insisting that it is in the public interest to expand methadone treatment, suggested that the obstacles to its expansion have increased as the program has shown evidence of success. He implied that organized crime may have something to do with this: "Who profits from the *status quo?* Whom are we hurting by stopping heroin use?"[27] He reported that FDA officers, responsible for evaluating the safety and efficacy of new drugs, said privately that there is actually no doubt about methadone treatment, and that the IND status was maintained only as an indirect means of controlling the abuse of methadone.[28] Similarly, Dr. John C. Cramer, running a California methadone program, called the experimental status a "fiction."[29] And, from the President's office, Jerome Jaffe asserted that "methadone has no more inherent danger than other drugs when they are abused."[30]

In June 1971, Charles Edwards, commissioner of the FDA, supported continuation of the IND status because existing data were inadequate in terms of the sample number of patients, the few studies of matched groups in different programs, and limited knowledge concerning the impact of the drug itself as compared to associated rehabilitative efforts.[31] But the pressure to change the IND status mounted, and, by November 1971, Edwards testified before the Senate Subcommittee on Public Health and Environment that continuing IND status was no longer defensible when methadone was in fact being used "as a regular part of the physician's armamentarium in combatting the heroin problem."[32] Toward the end of 1971 the FDA committed itself to taking a formal position on the safety and efficacy of methadone as a maintenance drug when it began to evaluate a New Drug Application (NDA) filed by the Eli Lilly Company for "diskets," a formulation of methadone hydrochloride in a tablet that dissolves in water and forms a sludge that cannot be drawn into a hypodermic needle.

The evaluation of methadone posed special problems for the FDA, first because of the possibilities of abuse, and second because of the difficulty in evaluating its efficacy. However, approval of a new drug application can include provisions for minimizing abuse by confining manufacturer distributions to registered recipients. This substitutes civil procedures of control for the criminal procedures presently in existence under the BNDD. But the problem of determining the efficacy of methadone is more difficult as long as its contribution to the rehabilitation of narcotics addicts remains debatable. Thus, FDA Commissioner Edwards made it clear that if the drug were to be approved, it should be approved not for its efficacy as a rehabilitation treatment, but only for its specific and demonstrated pharmacological effect.[33] Such qualified approval has precedent in the case of the antacid medicines sold for "symptomatic relief." With methadone already in wide use for maintenance purposes, the FDA was under pressure to approve the new drug application; alternatively, it would have to revoke many of the existing IND certificates. In December 1972 the FDA imposed federal guidelines under which methadone would be regarded no longer as an investigational drug, but as a "legitimate medical treatment." Programs would be expanded so that methadone would be available to all those who had been unable to find treatment, but much stricter controls would be established through a closed system of distribution limited to licensed practitioners. In fact this greatly increased the FDA control over methadone use, removing the drug from pharmacies and from private practice, and limiting its use to FDA-approved and supervised programs.

State Controls

The regulatory system is further complicated by state controls. In New York State, once a program receives FDA authorization, it must secure a certificate of approval to use the drug from the Commissioner of Mental Hygiene and the State Narcotics Control Bureau, an agency in the Department of Health which monitors safeguards concerning the possession of drugs. Also, approval to establish a medical research facility must come from the Public Health Council in consultation with the State Hospital Council of New York and the Environmental Engineering Section of the Department of Health. If a program requires a new medical facility, this must be approved by the Public Health Department which also supplies an operating certificate. Finally, a methadone program requires approval from the Narcotics Addiction Control Commission (NACC). This commission, set up as an autonomous body within the State Department of Mental Hygiene, is the major source of funds for drug-abuse programs; its resources as well as its ideological position on methadone are crucial to the development of this treatment.

The establishment of the NACC in 1966 was the first attempt in New York State to deal on a massive scale with the prevention, treatment, and control of the drug problem.[34] In the years following the establishment of NACC, drug abuse became a political issue, and among Governor Nelson Rockefeller's 1970 campaign promises was a "declaration of total war" on drugs and a commitment to earmark $15 million to provide full funding for methadone programs throughout the state.[35] Promises were followed by promotion and an "advance-man," Rayburn Hesse from the NACC's department of federal-state relations, traveled around upstate New York offering state funds for methadone maintenance outpatient programs. By 1971, $13.9 million had been allocated for such new programs. In addition, the NACC was using methadone to treat heroin addicts in its own civil and criminal commitment facilities.

In January 1971 state legislation provided that criminal proceedings against a person declared drug dependent could be waived in favor of voluntary commitment to a drug treatment program, and Rocke-feller announced that the state must "redouble its efforts to eradicate the dread cancer" of drug abuse.[36] But by April there were massive budget cuts in the NACC. Meanwhile Rayburn Hesse had been too successful in promoting new programs. Funding had been available in the first fiscal year following the 1970 election when few programs were tooled up to spend it. But those programs licensed by 1971 and 1972 and staffed with the expectation of adequate state funding found themselves in an awkward position. For the NACC funding policy, established on the basis of Rockefeller's campaign promises, was simply out of tune with state fiscal policy.

The total 1971–1972 NACC budget request for all drug-abuse and prevention programs was reduced from $163.2 million to $91.7 million, considerably less than the previous year's allocation of $117.2 million. All admissions to the NACC's own civil and criminal commitment facilities were suspended, and the agency was forced to close ten of them in September 1971, reducing its residential capacity from 6,000 to 2,200 beds and its staff from 5,147 to 3,992.

The budget cuts had two consequences: first, with fewer beds, the NACC was sending addicts back to their local communities, forcing increased applications for medicaid and welfare reimbursements. The message from the state seemed to be: "Junkie go home. Let the community deal with your problem." This was especially unfortunate since many county-level governments were reluctant to confront their drug problems. Second, there was increased pressure for less expensive outpatient approaches, and the relatively low-cost and efficient methadone maintenance treatment became increasingly attractive as a model.

Methadone maintenance was the only drug program that was not cut back by the new budget, but increases could not keep up with the demands of new programs. In 1971, New York State appropriated $19.7 million for twenty-two ambulatory methadone maintenance programs, with a capacity to serve 17,000 addicts. This appropriation averaged about $1,156 per patient per year, much less than the usual estimated cost of $1,800 to $2,000 per patient. The sum caused uncertainty for those who had committed themselves with staff and patients in anticipation of promised funds. Would programs get started only to be curtailed?[37] These concerns were exacerbated in November 1971 when the NACC sent a telegram to all methadone maintenance program directors throughout the state declaring that, in accord with the state wage freeze, no vacant positions could be filled until further notice and that all expenditures, even those within approved budgets, must be cleared directly with the NACC. Because of continuing pressures to increase the size of programs, and daily problems that often required immediate response, the telegram was regarded as a disaster.

The telegram suggested the commission's ambivalence toward methadone treatment, and in mid-December 1971 Howard A. Jones, NACC chairman, opposed the long-term use of a legal addictive drug, calling the rapid expansion of methadone maintenance programs "close to a surrender to the problem."[38] On the whole, however, the NACC retrenchment primarily affected educational and abstinence programs more than methadone maintenance. According to NACC officers, the budget cuts reflected "a clearly stated legislative intent to de-emphasize long-term residential treatment and rehabilitation, and place the accent instead on short-term detoxification, methadone maintenance, and expanded community treatments and rehabilitation services."[39]

Evaluations and Recommendations

Several groups have been systematically evaluating methadone maintenance programs, including the World Health Organization (WHO) Expert Committee, a group from the Columbia School of Public Health and Administrative Medicine, and the Committee on Alcoholism and Drug Dependence of the AMA in cooperation with the Committee on Problems of Drug Dependence of the National Research Council (NRC). The evaluations, based on surveys of some of the larger programs, have emphasized the success of the program for at least a segment of the addict population, and they all recommend expansion but with continued regulation.

The WHO evaluation in 1969 and again in 1970 regarded methadone maintenance with favor, but recommended that the treatment remain experimental because the patients involved were not representative of the drug-dependent population, being older, largely white, and better educated. The evaluation stated that the treatment was not suitable for use by private physicians, who could not afford to provide the support of "a multi-disciplinary medical service to effect therapeutic social, economic, and rehabilitative measures which may be necessary to check for possible relapse to multiple drug use."[40]

The AMA-NRC committees reported in 1967 and again in 1971. Their early position was cautious; they regarded methadone maintenance as promising for research, but did not consider it an established treatment. By 1971 they accepted the treatment status of methadone programs, emphasizing the need for continued regulation, evaluation, and research. They also felt that methadone maintenance was not feasible for private office practice because of the need for associated medical and psychiatric services.[41]

The New York City program has had ongoing evaluation by a group from Columbia University directed by Frances Rowe Gearing. In 1969 and again in 1970 they noted the high retention rate (80 percent of all the patients admitted remained in the program), the dramatic reduction in arrests, and the increases in employment. While the study also found evidence of continued drug abuse by at least 10 percent of the patients, and alcohol abuse by another 8 percent, the program was considered effective for most participants. Its continued development in combination with other treatment approaches was recommended. The second Columbia study in 1970 also recommended a demonstration project in which private physicians would, in an extension of an organized program, treat those patients with only limited need of ancillary services.[42]

The evaluations have themselves been subject to a kind of criticism that suggests the lack of professional consensus both on the objectives of the program and on appropriate measures of "success." Donald Louria, president of the New York State Council on Drug Addiction, notes that the data on which evaluations have been based are largely supplied by the programs themselves, with few mechanisms for outside verification.[43] Concerned with their public image (which may affect their continued funding), many rehabilitation programs are wary of outside evaluation. Others have had no resources for compiling systematically the data needed for evaluations. Also, the two primary measures of success have been criticized. Using the declining rate of arrests is questionable since police are often willing to

defer arraignment of an addict if he is in treatment.
Similarly the retention rate is labeled meaningless by
some critics, given the continuing physiological dependence on methadone.[44] The fact that methadone patients
are usually older than the average addict, and close to
the age at which it appears to be easier for addicts to
abstain from drugs without methadone, has caused some
skeptics to question the actual effectiveness of the
program. This maturation factor has significance both for
the prospects as well as the actual effect of the
methadone program.

Individual program evaluations suggest a number of
problems. In a New Orleans clinic, 36 percent of the
patients dropped out because of difficulties of traveling
to the clinic, boredom, and objections to program
management.[45] New York programs have set up
neighborhood clinics in ghetto communities, but these
pose special problems because of continuing peer
pressure. "Right next door to my building is the biggest
dope drop in Brooklyn and people can walk out of my
building and walk right next store and 'cop.'"[46] An
NACC study in 1970 of a group of stabilized methadone
patients over an eight-week period found them free of
drug use only 41 percent of the time; 14 percent of the
group resorted to regular daily heroin supplements of
their methadone dosage.[47]

An evaluation of a Philadelphia program found
continued use of heroin and other drugs among 97.4
percent of the patients, suggesting that drug craving had
not been significantly reduced.[48] Similarly, studies of
NIMH programs note little decline in the arrest rate and

a high rate of drug abuse.[49] Yet Robert DuPont, head of a Washington, D.C., methadone program, attributes a 5.2 percent decrease in serious crime in 1970 in that city to its large-scale methadone program.[50]

Program directors have shared their experiences in a series of national conferences on methadone treatment. Most abide by the AMA position, concluding that methadone maintenance programs should be restricted to special clinics, both to avoid abuse and to make available necessary supportive and rehabilitative services. Some, however, would like to see extension of the program to private practitioners as a means of reducing the demand for black market methadone. Vincent Dole, for example, wants to remove the program from its experimental status and to increase decentralization by experimenting with private arrangements.[51] And Robert G. Newman, director of the New York City methadone maintenance program for the Department of Health, claims that the need to make methadone widely available requires a major participation by the private sector of medicine. Concerned with the potential use of methadone as a means of social control, he argues that transferring the treatment from the government to the private sector, thereby increasing its availability, would help to minimize such abuse.[52] However, the new FDA classification precludes expansion of the program in the private sector.

Advocates of methadone treatment are enthusiastic, yet are usually careful to note that it is not a final solution for all drug addicts. The public response has been less reserved, both in support of and in opposition to the program. Methadone maintenance has won fervent approval by many who see it as an easy and almost magical solution to a national crisis, "paralleled in importance only by the discovery of penicillin in this century."[53] Equated with automatic rehabilitation, the public media welcomed methadone as a "bargain from society's standpoint,"[54] and a "Cinderella drug," noting the testimony of addicts who "speak reverently of the program as if it were a religious movement."[55] Similar concern with efficiency prompted a physician to note that financial wisdom dictates that we should "spend a dime to save a dollar."[56]

Opposition

There are, however, many who are strongly opposed to methadone programs, and for a number of reasons. Some argue that the introduction of methadone maintenance is a "*déjà vu* experience," for, long before methadone, both heroin and cocaine were advocated as a cure for opium addiction. In 1884, for example, Sigmund Freud prescribed massive doses of cocaine to relieve the problems of a friend addicted to morphine in the course of medical treatment.[57] Also at this time opium was recommended as a treatment for alcoholism on much the same grounds that the use of methadone is presently advocated. In 1889 a physician had noted that

opium is less inimical to a healthy life than alcohol; it calms in place of exciting the baser passions, and hence is less productive of acts of violence and crime. . . . On the score of economy the morphine habit is by far the better. . . . On the score then of saving to the individual and his family in immediate outlay, and of incurred disability, and of the great diminution of peace disturbers and of crime whereby an immense outlay will be saved by the state; on the score of decency of behavior instead of perverse devilry, of bland courtesy instead of vicious combativeness . . . I would urge the substitution of morphine instead of alcohol for all to whom such a craving is an incurable propensity.[58]

There were warnings about the danger of morphine as early as 1870. "The uncomfortable fear of mischief is growing," said Sir Thomas Clifford Allbutt, University of Cambridge Professor of Medicine.[59] But few were concerned.

Another objection to methadone maintenance is that a technological solution does not confront the real social and/or psychological problems that lead people to addiction in the first place. These critics view it as no more than a simple medical approach to a complex social, political, and psychological problem.[60] It is criticized as a short-sighted, patchwork treatment based on the principle of least effort, and one which "deepens prevailing mystifications by perpetuating the drug means for the solution of human problems."[61] From a psychiatric perspective chemical solutions merely permit addicts to transfer dependence without having to face up to themselves and to their problems. Many of these objections come from professional groups with an interest in diverting support to other types of rehabilitation programs. Daniel Casriel, the psychiatric superintendent at Daytop Village in New York City, calls the methadone treatment "malpractice and a cop-out," a cheap substitute for an expensive habit of self-indulgence. "When a narcotic is made free and available by government agencies it can only increase and encourage the further use of drugs." He regards the physician prescribing methadone as another pusher: "If we can't lick 'em . . . let's join 'em."[62]

Methadone maintenance has also been criticized by those concerned, for various reasons, with the workability of the program. Howard A. Jones, chairman of the NACC, expressed reservations about the rapid expansion of chemotherapeutic programs, on the grounds that the necessary ancillary services cannot keep pace.[63] David Ausubel argues that because methadone produces no euphoria, addicts will seek other drugs. He regards addicts as "inadequate personalities," unable to adjust voluntarily to "normal" life, and claims that prolonged compulsory "closed ward" treatment is necessary for those who are "apathetic, weakly motivated, unreliable, and irregular in keeping appointments."[64] I. C. Chein notes that "attention is so fixated on the drug that scarcely an eyebrow is lifted at the manifest paradox of patients cooperating with a treatment regime that deprives them of the psychic gratification for the sake of which they are supposedly impervious to treatment and cure."[65] And, finally, Alfred R. Lindesmith, pointing out that the syringe itself has symbolic associations for the addict, observes that narcotics bring social and psychological as well as physiological satisfaction to the user.[66] Methadone does not obliterate problems for the individual, and it provides none of the symbolic gratifications of heroin use. Thus, the question remains as to whether methadone can in the long run work as an effective substitute.

The issue of abuse has become a serious one. Methadone can be used by street addicts to reduce their heroin habit to a less expensive level. Methadone allowed out of the clinic is, therefore, marketable. From December 1969 through June 1970, BNDD purchases and seizures of illegally possessed methadone totaled 8,202 dosage units. From July 1970 to January 1971, the seizures totaled 33,981 dosage units. A *New York Times* survey of fourteen cities with methadone programs found all of them to have significant traffic in the drug.[67]

Illegally used methadone is primarily of legitimate manufacture, since it is difficult to synthesize the drug clandestinely. The illegal supply apparently comes either from patients in methadone programs or from loose prescription practices by physicians. For example, one physician claimed to have treated 15,000 patients. He was arrested and charged with dispensing methadone without adequate evidence that his patients were addicted. (The charges were eventually dropped.)

Methadone clinics may inadvertently be responsible for abuse. The availability of a quick solution, it is argued, minimizes the risk of addiction, and may encourage drug experimentation. Furthermore, Donald Louria claims that because of the low quality of street heroin, many users are not actually physiologically addicted. A program risks, then, turning nonaddicted heroin users into methadone addicts.[68] This possibility is suggested by a study of admissions to the NIMH clinical research center at Lexington, Kentucky. Out of one hundred consecutive admissions of opiate users in January 1971, forty-three showed no actual physical dependence when tested. There are no adequate diagnostic techniques for determining the extent of addiction or the tolerance to narcotics.[69] Verbal claims of patients are notoriously unreliable, and if in fact the patient has no tolerance to sustain the methadone, he may die of an overdose. Indeed, in 1970 and 1971, at least twenty-five people in New York City died of methadone overdose and five of these deaths occurred after taking the drug in a clinic. And in January and February 1972 fourteen deaths were attributed directly to methadone.[70] Although obviously less of a problem than heroin deaths, they have become a matter of special concern. In October 1971 the methadone overdose of an eighteen-year-old student in Texas following a visit to a clinic prompted an investigation which revealed that the victim was not a heroin addict. He had been given a prescription for methadone without a prior medical examination. The case was ruled a homicide, and at the time of this writing, the Austin grand jury was considering an indictment for murder of the doctor who wrote the prescription.

It can be argued that the illegal distribution of clinic methadone is not entirely disadvantageous. Generally addicts feel that it is less desirable than heroin and use it primarily to reduce their heroin needs, and therefore their need to steal. However, this indication of abuse fostered by a legal distribution system is regarded as politically unacceptable, and the potentiality of such abuse has become the major argument against the methadone program.

Objections to methadone maintenance programs are also made on political grounds. United States Congressman Charles B. Rangel has observed that methadone as a cheap solution seems to be a therapy designed for blacks and an example of how special standards are used in dealing with the problems of the poor. In public hearings he questions what would be done if a more affluent economic group were affected by a similar problem, and he advocates limiting the expansion of methadone.[71]

Politicized black groups regard addicts as ineffective for political activity and highly vulnerable to control. Thus they strongly oppose all programs based on stabilizing the addictive conditions. They call methadone a "white man's opiate" and the treatment "a form of genocide," "a colonial device," and an attempt to "stone the black community and make them sterile."[72] A black doctor who began a program in Bedford-Stuyvesant described his reception as "the black man who had been chosen by the white man to deliver the white man's poison to that community."[73] From this perspective the program is merely the introduction of yet another drug into black neighborhoods and a means of fostering subservience rather than strength of will within the black community. In December 1971 a national conference of black physicians and health-care workers, sponsored by two medical colleges, Howard and Meharry, concluded that the methadone maintenance program was "an attempt to control large segments of the non-white population through submissive behavior."[74]

Many see a form of "medical blackmail" in the fact that a patient can be suspended from a program for reasons defined by those in control. In a controversial presentation to the Third National Conference on Methadone Treatment, Robert Newman, director of the New York City Health Department's methadone maintenance program, observed that "the likelihood of such medical blackmail is increased by the intermingling of medical and social goals which certain programs set for themselves."[75]

The controversy over methadone maintenance reflects the tangle of often irreconcilable legal, moral, political, and medical attitudes toward addiction and its treatment. But it also reflects the views of the partisans of various rehabilitation approaches, each committed to a particular technique and competing for limited financial resources. As methadone maintenance receives an increasing share of these resources, the controversy is sharpened, particularly at the level of individual clinics as they are established. The rest of this study will examine how these issues interact within a particular program, and how that program relates to the surrounding community.

NOTES

[1]Information on the early development of the methadone program is available in numerous articles by Vincent Dole, M.D., and Marie Nyswander, M.D., including: Vincent Dole, M.D., "In the Course of Professional Practice," *New York State Journal of Medicine*, 65 (April 1, 1965), 927–931; Vincent Dole, M.D., and Marie Nyswander, M.D., "A Medical Treatment for Diacetylmorphine (Heroin) Addiction," *Journal of the American Medical Association*, 193 (August 23, 1965), 646–650; Vincent Dole, M.D.,

"Methadone Maintenance Treatment for 25,000 Addicts," *Journal of the American Medical Association*, 215 (February 15, 1971), 1131–1150; Marie Nyswander, M.D., "The Methadone Treatment of Heroin Addiction," *Hospital Practice*, 2 (April 1967); Vincent Dole, M.D., and Marie Nyswander, M.D., "Rehabilitation of Heroin Addicts after Blockade with Methadone," *New York State Journal of Medicine*, 66 (August 1, 1966), 2011–2017. For a bibliography of articles concerning methadone maintenance, see Stanley Einstein, ed., *Methadone Maintenance* (Second National Methadone Maintenance Conference, New York: Marcel Dekker, 1971), 235–245; and "Methadone: a Bibliography 1929–1971;" *International Journal of the Addictions*, 6 (June 1971), 329–345. See also the National Association for the Prevention of Addiction to Narcotics (NAPAN) *Proceedings*, Third National Conference on Methadone Treatment, 1970, and Fourth National Conference on Methadone Treatment, 1972.

[2]Avraim Goldstein, "The Pharmacological Basis of Methadone Treatment," in *NAPAN, Proceedings*, 1972, pp. 27–32.

[3]Marvin Lipkowitz, *et al.*, "Abrupt Withdrawal of Methadone Maintenance," *Journal of the American Medical Association* 217 (September 27, 1971), 1860–1861. Note, however, that this is based on a sample of only four cases.

[4]Vincent Dole, M.D., "Research on Methadone Maintenance Treatment," *International Journal of the Addictions*, 5 (September 1970), pp. 359–373; and Thomas Muskelly, "Motivations and their Relationship to Methadone Maintenance Withdrawal Problems," in *NAPAN, Proceedings*, 1972, pp. 177–179.

[5]G. Blinick, R. Wallace, and E. Jerez, "Pregnancy in Narcotics Addicts Treated by Medical Withdrawal," *American Journal of Obstetrics and Gynecology*, 105 (December 1969), 997–1003.

[6]Letter to the Editor from David Annunziato, *Pediatrics*, 47 (April 1971), 787, and *Herald Tribune* (International Edition), March 2, 1972.

[7]Quoted in Nat Hentoff, *A Doctor among the Addicts* (New York: Grove Press, Evergreen Black Cat ed. 1968), p. 44.

[8]Frances Rowe Gearing, M.D., "Methadone Maintenance Treatment Program: Progress Report through March 31, 1971—A Five Year Overview" (mimeographed), p. 2. The Beth-Israel program runs fifteen hospitals and forty clinics. In addition, the New York City Health Service admits nearly 6,000 patients.

[9]Project Management Staff, New York City Health Service, "Methadone Maintenance Treatment Program Implementation Project" (mimeographed, May 20, 1971).

[10]S. B. Sells and Deena D. Watson, "A Specturum of Approaches in Methadone Treatment: Relation to Program Evaluation," in NAPAN, *Proceedings*, Third National Conference on Methadone Treatment, 1970, pp.

17–18, and Vincent Dole, M.D., "Planning for the Treatment of 25,000 Heroin Addicts," in *NAPAN, Proceedings*, 1970, p. 113.

[11]Herbert Kleber, "The New Haven Methadone Maintenance Program," in Stanley Einstein, ed., *Methadone Maintenance* (New York: Marcel Dekker, 1971). p. 104.

[12]Gerald E. Davidson, statement on "Narcotics Research, Rehabilitation, and Treatment," in U.S. House of Representatives, Select Committee on Crime, *Hearings*, 92nd Congress, 1st session, April 1971, Part 1, p. 326.

[13]The New York City waiting list has been estimated as high as 15,000, but this is difficult to determine since different agencies compile their lists in different ways depending on whether or not they include applications prior to interviewing, and addicts apply to several programs. There are holding stations in which addicts are given methadone prior to admission to a regular clinic.

[14]Jerome Jaffe, M.D., "Methadone Maintenance: Variation in Outcome, Criteria as a Function of Dose," in NAPAN, *Proceedings* 1970, p. 37.

[15]William F. Wieland and Arthur D. Moffett, "Results of Low Dosage Methadone Treatment," in NAPAN, *Proceedings* 1970, p. 49.

[16]Sells and Watson, *op. cit.*, p. 18.

[17]See especially David E. Smith *et al.*, "Adolescent Heroin Abuse in San Francisco," in NAPAN, *Proceedings*, 1970, p. 91.

[18]Marvin E. Perkins and Marriet Block, "A Study of some Failures in Methadone Treatment," *American Journal of Psychiatry* 128 (July 1971), 79–81.

[19]Avram Goldstein, "Blind Controlled Dosage Comparisons with Methadone in Two Hundred Patients" (mimeographed), p. 3.

[20]See Paul D. Gewirtz, "Methadone Maintenance for Heroin Addicts," *Yale Law Journal*, 78 (June 1969), 1184ff, for study of aspects of the legal and administrative structure of methadone programs.

[21]*Federal Register*, 36, No. 64, Friday, April 2, 1971, pp. 6075–6077.

[22]Prior to this act, a tax stamp was required through the Internal Revenue Service of the Department of the Treasury.

[23]Position reported in letter to the author from Edward Lewis, Jr., M.D., chief medical officer of the Bureau of Narcotics and Dangerous Drugs, September 23, 1971.

[24]FDA guidelines for specific conditions for the use of methadone appear in *Federal Register, op. cit.*, pp. 6075–6077.

[25]See statement by Charles C. Edwards, Commissioner, FDA, in U.S. House of Representatives, Committee on Interstate and Foreign Commerce, Subcommittee on Public Health and Environment, *Hearings*, 92nd Congress, 1st session, November 8, 1971, pp. 1496–1501.

[26]Letter to the Editor from Edward A. Noll, M.D., *Journal of American Medical Association*, 215 (February 15, 1971), 1159.

[27]Vincent Dole, M.D., "Research on Methadone Maintenance Treatment," *International Journal of the Addictions*, 5 (September 1970), 371.

[28]Vincent P. Dole, M.D., "Planning for the Treatment of 25,000 Heroin Addicts," in NAPAN, *Proceedings*, 1970, p. 112. Although subsequent testimony by Edwards suggested this was apparently the case, it is interesting that there is no system to provide for cooperation between the FDA and the BNDD and very few situations in which cases of illegal dispensing were reported by the FDA to the BNDD.

[29]Select Committee on Crime, *Hearings, op. cit.*, June 1971, p. 644.

[30]*New York Times*, November 9, 1971.

[31]Statement by Charles C. Edwards, in Select Committee on Crime, *Hearings, op. cit.*, June 2, 1971, p. 395.

[32]Statement by Charles C. Edwards in Subcommittee on Public Health and Environment, *Hearings, op. cit.*, November 1971, p. 1499.

[33]*Ibid.*, p. 7.

[34]NACC, *Annual Report*, 1969, p. 2.

[35]Most of the programs supported by the NACC are funded on a fifty-fifty matching basis with local support. NACC, *Attack*, Winter 1970, lists other programs.

[36]NACC, *Attack*, (Fall–Winter 1971), 1.

[37]At about this time a program in Gainesville, Florida, which had been running for a year, was suspended because of "bureaucratic technicalities." It had thirty-seven addicts on methadone. A nonaddictive drug was administered to ease withdrawal but this had "obvious side-effects." The program was started again in six days. *Gainesville Sun*, October 10, 1971.

[38]*New York Times*, Section E, January 2, 1972, p. 8.

[39]NACC, "Agency Appraisal Report" (mimeographed, 1971). Realization of the excessive demands on states such as New York stimulated introduction of a bill which would allow emergency federal assistance to states to set up methadone maintenance facilities.

[40]World Health Organization Expert Committee on Drug Dependence, 16th Report, WHO Technical Report Series, 1969.

[41]Combined Statement of the AMA Council on Mental Health and its Committee on Alcoholism and Drug Dependence and NAS-NRC Committee on Problems of Drug Dependence, "Oral Methadone Maintenance Techniques in the Management of Morphine-Type Dependence" (mimeographed), p. 2. For the attitudes of individual physicians, see NAPAN, *Proceedings*, 1970 and 1972, *passim*, and Einstein, *op. cit.*

[42]Frances Rowe Gearing, M.D., "Methadone Maintenance Treatment Program: Progress Report through March 31, 1971—A Five-Year Overview," submitted to NACC (mimeographed, May 14, 1971), p. 8.

[43]Donald Louria, *Overcoming Drugs* (New York: McGraw-Hill, 1971), pp. 198ff.

[44]William R. Martin, "Commentary on the Second National Conference on Methadone Treatment," in Einstein, *op. cit.*, p. 200.

[45]Richard Adams, *et. al.*, "Heroin Addiction on Methadone: A Study of Drop-outs," *International Journal of the Addictions*, 6 (June 1971), 269–277.

[46]Beny J. Primm, "Ancillary Services in Methadone Treatment: The Bedford-Stuyvesant Experience," in NAPAN, *Proceedings*, 1970, p. 68.

[47]Testimony by Howard A. Jones, Select Committee on Crime, *Hearings, op. cit.*, part 2, p. 587.

[48]Carl D. Chambers and W. J. Russell Taylor, "Patterns of Cheating among Methadone Maintenance Patients," presented at Eastern Psychiatric Research Association, November 7-8, 1970.

[49]Richard Phillipson, M.D., "Methadone Maintenance Programs funded by the National Institute of Mental Health," presented at Methadone Workshop, Portland, March 27, 1971 (mimeographed), pp. 2, 6, 7.

[50]Robert L. DuPont, M.D., "Heroin Addiction Treatment and Crime Reduction," *American Journal of Psychiatry*, 128 (January 1972), 90ff.

[51]See statement by Dr. Robert L. DuPont, Select Committee on Crime, *Hearings, op. cit.*, Part 1, p. 147. Also see Vincent Dole, M.D., "Methadone Maintenance Treatment for 25,000 Addicts," *Journal of the American Medical Association*, 215 (February 15, 1971), 1133.

[52]Robert G. Newman, "Methadone Maintenance Treatment: Special Problems of Government-Controlled Programs," in NAPAN, *Proceedings*, 1970, p. 124, and "Expansion of Publicly Funded Methadone Programs—Will It Be Enough?" NAPAN, *Proceedings*, 1972, pp. 73–75.

[53]Robert F. Horan, Jr., criticizes this attitude in Select Committee on Crime, *Hearings, op. cit.*, Part 1, p. 256.

[54]E. K. Faltermayer, "Some Here and Now Steps to Cut Crime," *Fortune*, 82 (July 1970), 94–99, 136–139.

[55]Roland H. Berg, "New Hope for Drug Addicts," *Look*, November 30, 1965 (reprint).

[56]James L. Mathis, M.D., "Comment," *American Journal of Psychiatry* 128 (January 1972), 90ff.

[57]Ernest Jones, M.D., *The Life and Work of Sigmund Freud* (New York: Basic Books, 1953), I. 85–95.

[58]J. K. Black, M.D., *Cincinnati Lancet Clinic*, 1889, quoted in Richard Phillipson, M.D., "Methadone Maintenance: Why Continue Controls?" in NAPAN, *Proceedings*, 1970, pp. 1–2.

[59]Quoted in Norman Howard Jones, "The Origins of Hypodermic Medication," *Scientific American*, 224 (January 1971), 102.

[60]Harriet Block and Lester Wallerstein, "Two Treatments: Methadone vs. Therapeutic Communities," *Health/Pac Bulletin*, June 1970, p. 18.

[61]Henry L. Lennard *et al.*, *Mystification and Drug Abuse* (San Francisco: Jossey-Bass, 1971), p. 97.

[62]Daniel Casriel, M.D., testifying before the House of Representatives, Select Committee on Crime, *Hearings*, 92nd Congress, 1st Session, 1971, Part 1, pp. 296–297.

[63]Press interview in *New York Times*, December 19, 1971.

[64]David P. Ausubel, M.D., "Why Compulsory Closed-Ward Treatment of Narcotic Addicts?" State of New York Narcotic Addiction Control Commission pamphlet, June 1968, p. 7.

[65]Isador Chein, "Psychological Functions of Drug Use," H. Steinberg, ed., *Scientific Basis of Drug Dependence* (London: Churchill, 1969), pp. 13–30.

[66]Alfred R. Lindesmith, *Addiction and Opiates* (Chicago: Aldine, 1968), pp. 129–155.

[67]*New York Times*, January 2, 1972. See reports of accidental deaths and bootleg problems in *Boston Sunday Herald-Traveller*, April 11, 1971; *Boston Evening Globe*, April 22, 1971; see also Jacob Hoogerbeets, "Methadone in Miami," in Einstein, *op. cit.*, p. 155.

[68]Donald Louria, *Overcoming Drugs*, (New York: McGraw-Hill, 1971), p. 82. For the dangers of converting "week-end" heroin users to hard-core addicts, see V. Marks, D. Fry, and P. Chappel, "Application of Urine Analysis to Diagnosis and Treatment of Heroin Addicts," *British Medical Journal*, 2 (1969), 153–155.

[69]Ramon Gardiner and P. H. Connell, "One Year's Experience in a Drug Dependence Clinic," *The Lancet*, August 29, 1970, pp. 455–458. Also see Richard Phillipson, "Methadone Maintenance: Some Uses, Some Limitations, Some Dangers," International Symposium on Drug Tolerance Addiction Abuse and Methadone Treatment, New Orleans, August 17, 1971 (mimeographed).

[70]*New York Times*, February 4, 1972, and March 14, 1972. See also David Frazer, "Methadone Overdose," *Journal of the American Medical Association*, 217 (September 6, 1971), 1387–1389.

[71]Statement by Congressman Charles Rangel, Select Committee on Crime, *Hearings, op. cit.*, July 1971, *passim*.

[72]See, for example, a letter to the *New England Journal of Medicine*, 281 (August 14, 1969), by Steven Jonas, reported in Einstein, *op. cit.*, pp. 208–209.

[73]Beny J. Primm, M.D., "Ancillary Services in Methadone Treatment: Bedford-Stuyvesant Experience," in NAPAN, *Proceedings*, 1970. p. 67.

[74]Reported in *New York Times*, December 13, 1971.

[75]Robert G. Newman, "Methadone Maintenance Treatment: Special Problems of Government-Controlled Programs," in NAPAN, *Proceedings*, 1970, p. 123. Note that this was regarded as a highly controversial point at the conference and was rebutted by other participants.

III / *Problems, Politics, and Treatment Programs: A Community Study*

On November 10, 1971, the press in Syracuse, New York dramatically revealed that a police investigation had found one hundred students at a white middle-class high school who were heroin users. The consequent public reaction revealed a great deal about local attitudes toward the drug problem, attitudes which have significantly influenced the implementation of methadone maintenance in a community.

Several weeks before the press announcement, the police had picked up a dealer carrying a list of student customers. At this time the district's legislator appeared on television to bring the problem to public attention. But the Syracuse newspapers, traditionally supportive of the successful Republican party in the city and reluctant to call attention to a controversial and potentially disruptive political matter, did not follow up the story until after the November election. Elections over, the press responded to the police disclosure with several hundred column inches of coverage in two days. There were dramatic editorials. "We fought a rising panic. Scores of parents, we know, felt like rushing home to question the current high school members of their families, to look for signs of use." One editorial estimated that 25 percent of Syracuse students were on hard drugs; another attacked "the Typhoid Marys of the drug business."[1] And yet another noted that Iran dealt effectively with dope peddlers by shooting anyone convicted of illegal possession of three and one half ounces of heroin; "quite a contrast to the slap on the wrist penalties imposed by the courts in this country."[2]

The police announced their tactics. There would be a moratorium on arrests of young drug users. The first step would be to bring the problem to the attention of parents and to request that they handle it. If a follow-up visit suggested that nothing had been done, rehabilitation procedures would be recommended. Members of the black community responded to this "white glove treatment" with resentment, asking how often policemen had tried to visit the parents of black kids caught using heroin. "If it was Central School, there would be mass arrests and cops in the hallways." But District Attorney Leo G. Hayes, hitherto known for his punitive attitude toward addiction, declared, "Law enforcement alone is never going to solve the drug problem."[3] And

Mayor Lee Alexander expressed his regret that "in the past, when drug use was thought confined to poors and blacks, society reacted with harsh punitive measures. Society now has come to the realization that the need for understanding and rehabilitation is of utmost importance."[4]

Other groups were mobilized by the incident. The Syracuse Chamber of Commerce offered to create a program to reward individuals who would provide information leading to the arrest of drug pushers. And the joint City-Onondaga County Drug Commission decided to conduct an epidemiological study to find out the extent of drug abuse in the metropolitan area, despite some concern that the results might be politically unappetizing if heroin were found to be prevalent in middle-class communities. Suburban officials, however, carefully emphasized that drugs were a city problem: "Our problem is not overwhelming . . . his [the Syracuse police chief's] problems are different than ours . . . much greater." On the authority of his own children, a suburban police chief said, "There is not a hard drug problem in our school system."[5]

The drug problem in Syracuse, as elsewhere, has been long-standing but poorly understood, rooted in the social, political, and economic structure of the community. The response to the police disclosure of November 1971 indicates the community ambivalence toward this frustrating problem, but its visible increase created a growing sense of crisis calling for decisive action to resolve it at all costs. The details of the response suggest the process by which solutions are explored, existing arrangements adapted, and new programs emerge.[6]

Local Conditions and
the Problem of Addiction

The exact number of heroin addicts in Syracuse is, of course, unknown. The Police Department figures indicate 400 mainlining addicts and 1,000 users; other estimates range from 200 to 800 addicts, a discrepancy in part resting on the vague differentiation between heroin use and addiction. In a survey in 1970 of 15,000 high school students, 178 students admitted to having tried heroin, and 118 to having sold it. The estimates of heroin addiction are increasing, but it is difficult to know the extent to which this represents a real trend or reflects more energetic policing, for narcotics arrests have been increasing rapidly for the last few years. In Onondaga County, state police arrested 140 persons on narcotics offenses in 1968, 203 in 1969, and 226 in 1970. City police arrested 24 in 1966, 128 in 1968, 115 in 1969, and 150 in 1970. Seventy-two suspected heroin dealers were arrested in the first ten months of 1971. During an eighteen-month period in 1970–1971, 239 people were convicted of drug-related charges in County Court, 80 of whom were youthful offenders (i.e., under nineteen years old) with a clean record. About a third of the case load in local courts is now related to drug abuse.

The large-scale use of heroin in Syracuse, unlike the use of other drugs, has been concentrated in the black inner city. Social and economic patterns within this area reveal some pressures which might stimulate addiction. Between 1950 and 1960 the nonwhite population increased by 143 percent, and it nearly doubled again (93 percent) in the period from 1960 to 1970 (see Table 3).

Table 3.   Population changes in Syracuse, 1950–1970[*]

	1950	1960	1970
White	215,525	203,757	173,577
Nonwhite	5,058	12,281	23,720
Total	220,583	216,038	197,297
% Nonwhite	2.3	5.7	12.02

[*]U.S. Census, 1970.

As whites left the central city, the black population concentrated in inner-city districts. In 1950, 80 percent of the nonwhite population lived in only four of the city's sixty-one census tracts, and by 1960 the population in these same four districts had doubled. The area of concentration shifted in the early 1960's as a result of urban renewal, but the pattern of concentration continued. Moreover, the process of relocation was traumatic and sparked civil rights demonstrations. Housing conditions in these areas have been described as comparing unfavorably with other nonwhite areas in upstate New York.[7]

Approximately 25 percent of the Syracuse black

population are on welfare, and 40 percent are below the poverty level, although overall wages in Syracuse in recent years compare favorably with U.S. average wages.[8] Urban renewal stimulated development of construction and manufacturing industries, but these changes had little effect on black employment: in 1960 only 2.7 percent earned over $6,000, and only 2 percent were in a professional/technical category.[9] Black employment did increase in the latter part of the 1960's, but only for limited sections of the population—professional people, office workers, and "entry level" factory workers.[10] During this time employment of unskilled labor decreased, and during periods of recession the black unemployment rate has been as high as 18.5 percent.

Politically, blacks have limited power; in 1971 there were no black elected officials, and there were only six black patrolmen on the 469-member police force. The one black-run newspaper, *Home-town News*, ceased publication when its editor, Chris Powell, died in 1969. It was replaced by the *Gazette*, a paper directed to the black community but edited by the white director of the Model Cities Program. In the traditionally conservative city, black community leaders are seldom brought in to make decisions concerning their own interests. According to Allen Campbell, Dean of the Maxwell School of Syracuse University, the black community is simply too small to develop enough professionals to serve its best interests: "By almost any measure, the black community in Syracuse is more disadvantaged than any other community here and in other communities in nearby cities."[11] Considering the political impotence of the black community, it is not surprising that the existence of a drug problem concentrated in the inner city evoked little response except from the police. Some blacks suggest that even the police tended to ignore it until its impact extended beyond the inner city.

Crime and Punishment

The Syracuse police chief has estimated that hard-core addicts are responsible for about an $18 million loss to the city annually through crimes committed to purchase drugs.[12] These crimes involve not only individual addicts who steal to support their own habit, but also a complex set of institutions including a network of drug pushers, and various arrangements for the handling of stolen goods. The police attribute 75 percent of the city's crime to addicts. Legal constraints and the fact that heroin can be produced efficiently in small quantities foster small distribution units managed by a centralized but well-protected monopoly. The task of controlling the local distribution as well as the criminal activities of addicts is primarily the responsibility of the organized crime division of the City Police Department. The annual cost of control is estimated by the department at about $500,000. Drug units are also found in the State Police and in the County Sheriff's Department, each with its own separate funding and jurisdiction. Fragmented jurisdictional control has caused serious problems of coordination and duplication, and there is discussion of creating a joint city-county narcotics squad.

The city police work primarily through undercover

agents and also depend on informants. They have a full-time narcotics squad of about seventeen men, yet virtually all policemen find themselves involved with drug problems. The ethnic makeup of the police force, their training, and their perceptions of their role equip them inadequately, however, for handling the complexities of the problem.[13] Police orientation is punitive; in the words of Chief Thomas Sardino, "All indications point to stiffer penalties and more stringent interpretation of existing laws for chronic offenders. . . . The laws of the land will not let them destroy themselves with drug misuse."[14] A strictly punitive approach to drug addiction becomes increasingly complicated, however, as the problem extends beyond the point where it can be effectively handled through the court system. This is frustrating for the police, who also consider their task unnecessarily complicated by public criticism and by difficulties of collecting sufficient legal evidence to make convictions. They believe that the community at large fails to understand the difficulty of controlling the seemingly endless source of heroin in the city. Furthermore, policemen tend to be unsympathetic to rehabilitation approaches and resent the "idealism" of rehabilitation workers. For example, the local officer of the state BNDD, who works with police on drug problems, refers to addicts as "the criminal element" and "pimps"; "The theory is that you can rehabilitate addicts; in practice, you can't." Rehabilitation programs, he claims, only make addicts *seem* respectable; where methadone is concerned, "they will abuse it as soon as controls are loosened up."[15]

By the time the methadone program began in

Syracuse, there was the beginning of some cooperation between the police and rehabilitation agencies. Although many officers regard a methadone patient as "just another junkie," the city department has agreed to call their program if a patient is arrested. Originally a staff member could deliver methadone to the jail in order to detoxify the patient. When this practice was stopped by state narcotics authorities who objected to the transporting of methadone, police cooperated by bringing handcuffed prisoners to the clinic, or by using methadone to detoxify the addict in jail. The interests of the police and rehabilitation workers are, however, in direct conflict. The police must seek information to facilitate arrests, while rehabilitation programs must protect their clients in order to maintain their confidence. Thus, police are excluded from weekly meetings at which the staffs of rehabilitation agencies and others concerned with the drug problem in Syracuse discuss their programs and problems. These staffs recognize, however, that police cooperation is crucial, and they raised the question at one meeting of whether to invite a police representative in order to encourage such cooperation. The response was overwhelmingly negative. Participants suspected that the police would use the meetings to get information for their own purposes. Moreover, those working with addicts in rehabilitation programs claimed that if their patients knew that they associated with the police, they would lose credibility. "Cops are cops first; even if their intentions are good, they get brownie points for busting people. . . . We can do ten good things, and then the first bad thing we do, we lose. . . . Our priorities are not to bust people." Yet some rehabilitation workers feel strongly that police are not exerting enough pressure to get people off the streets: "We lose people because the fuzz puts no pressure on addicts. We want them to put pressure on, but we can't help them to make arrests." The consensus of the meeting was: "Whichever cop comes to the meeting, he will need long legs to jump over the credibility gap."

A police officer was eventually invited to one meeting; the purpose was to inform him of rehabilitation efforts and to elicit police cooperation in directing addicts to programs. The officer himself agreed that it would be extremely awkward to maintain continuing contact, for he too was concerned with credibility; if he did not return with useful information, his department and the mayor's office would be suspicious of him.

Narcopolitics

During the spring of 1970, New York State passed provision 213A of the Mental Hygiene Law providing for state aid on a matching basis to start drug rehabilitation programs in local communities. The legislation required a coordinating unit, and the Onondaga County Legislature designated the County Department of Mental Health to develop a comprehensive treatment program. This department, originally the Mental Health Board, had been created in 1955 as a formal means of channeling state funds into local mental health services. Its early development reflected old tensions between professional and politically-oriented groups in Syracuse.[16] The rapid expansion of professional services at increasing cost to the county had been viewed with political disfavor and, in 1960, when appropriations were requested to hire a full-time psychiatrist, county supervisors had balked and assumed direct control over the Board's fiscal policies. When the metropolitan government was reorganized, the Mental Health Board became a county department.

The legislature, however, still regards new programs calling for long-term financial support with skepticism. The Onondaga County Legislature consists of twelve city and twelve county representatives. The area is traditionally Republican; the 1970 ratio of fifteen Republicans to nine Democrats increased in the 1971 elections to nineteen Republicans and five Democrats. The legislature has tended to turn away from dealing with controversial social problems, and the city has had a rocky history in dealing with its poor. For example, though Syracuse was one of the first communities to have an OEO antipoverty program, the Crusade for Opportunity, it was also the first to abandon it owing to growing conflict between black community leaders and the white power structure.[17] It is not surprising, therefore, that the politically conservative legislature ignored the existence of a drug problem in Syracuse. Then, early in 1970, two legislators proposed a Narcotics Guidance Council to set up a coordinated and continuing drug program. Five prominent citizens were brought together to provide leadership. But the Council received no legislative support and was forced to limit its activities to developing adult education programs. It never applied for state funds and did not use $11,000 made available to it by the state in 1970.

In June 1970, Mayor Alexander of Syracuse appointed a Temporary Commission on Narcotics Abuse and Addiction which included members of the medical and academic communities and of the police department. Their report in October 1970 recommended a City-County Coordinating Commission on Drug Abuse; this was duly established with sixteen members, selected equally by the county executive and the city mayor. Chaired by Michael Reagen from Syracuse University, the commission includes a school superintendent, a psychiatrist, a county sheriff, the city police chief, the district attorney, a bank president, the radio station manager, a pastor, the executive director of the Spanish Action League, and the commissioner of the Department of Mental Health. The commission reports directly to the mayor and the county executive, and its mandate is to act as a review board and coordinating agency for drug-abuse programs, a clearing house for information about available services, and to be a "sounding board" and a stimulus for new approaches in dealing with the drug dilemma in the city and in Onondaga County. It also makes recommendations to the Syracuse Common Council and the County Legislature relating to treatment, rehabilitation, education, and law enforcement. The commission, however, has been criticized as a legislative attempt to neutralize the drug issue—to bury the problem in expertise. Specifically, those who represent black constituencies as well as those involved

in specific treatment programs resent that they are not
directly represented on the commission. The commission is also hampered by its lack of staff. Inadequately
funded by the legislature, it operates primarily on a
$5,000 private donation.

There are a number of reasons for the apathy of the
legislature, apart from its traditional reluctance to
become involved in controversial social issues. First,
county representatives tend not to engage in issues
which they consider primarily city problems. Second,
they hesitate to put government funds into new
programs, even with matching state or federal support.
For "seed money" carries the implication that once
committed to a program, the county may have to pick up
the entire tab at some future time.

It is a measure of the growing political importance of
the drug-abuse problem that in 1970 the legislature
agreed to provide local funds to match state aid for
several drug-abuse programs (see Table 6). Donald
Boudreau, a psychiatrist and head of the Department of
Mental Health, had been sensitized to drug problems in
Syracuse largely through the activities of Henry Jackson,
a former addict and alumnus of the New York City
self-help therapeutic community, Daytop Village. Jackson had been seeking support for a drug-abstinence
program called Direction and Education of Narcotics
(DEN) since 1968, with little success. Taking advantage
of growing public concern about drugs, Boudreau began
to negotiate for state aid on a matching basis for DEN
and Argosy House, a residential and therapeutic
community also based on abstinence from narcotics. He

also sought to designate beds for addicts in the county hospital. As a part of his investigation of treatment possibilities, Dr. Boudreau visited the Beth-Israel methadone maintenance program.

Professional Politics:
The Rehabilitation System

The drug-abuse programs which developed during 1970 in Syracuse encompassed the existing range of treatments. They comprise the system in which the methadone maintenance program operates, and on which it depends for referrals and community contacts.

DEN, supported initially by the Community Chest Urban Crisis Fund, and later by the Junior League, was the first rehabilitation program for drug addicts in Syracuse, and the organization with the most day-to-day contact with the addict community. An inner-city, street-level organization, DEN seeks to identify heroin users, to bring them to a detoxification program, and then to provide regular follow-up and counseling services. It is committed to drug-free rehabilitation and uses confrontation techniques to force the addict to resolve his problems. Their creed is to "live life, and not just to stop drugs." Because addicts frequently return to the same community after being detoxified, only to become readdicted, Jackson has attempted to turn DEN into a new community for former addicts. Staff members, former addicts themselves, cover the Syracuse ghetto to maintain continuing contact with DEN members, who return regularly to the organization to participate in social events and to help with the rehabilitation of new members.

Argosy House, founded in February 1970, is also a therapeutic community staffed by former addicts and committed to total abstinence, but it is primarily for young people on drugs other than heroin. Argosy House maintains a storefront, a residential community for teenagers, and a day-care center which serves as an indoctrination center for new residents and as a base for those who are not in residence. The house itself is a "total community"; for a year to sixteen months participants are isolated and participate in encounter groups and other therapeutic measures directed toward emotional growth. After the year of residency, the staff assists patients in finding jobs or training and in reestablishing their relationships with family and community.

Other Syracuse groups working with addicts include Catholic Social Services, which has an informal personal counseling program; 1012, a crisis prevention center and crash pad at Syracuse University; a neighborhood health clinic; the NACC civil commitment program, which maintains contact with about one hundred addicts in the area; and a detoxification unit in St. Mary's Hospital. This unit was set up in February 1971 in a locked sixteen-bed ward in the small Catholic hospital. The program, which detoxified about one hundred patients in its first ten months of operation, works with patients for twenty-one days. During the first week, the addict is detoxified with the help of decreasing doses of methadone; the rest of the time is devoted to rehabilitation and counseling. However, about 30 percent of the patients leave before the twenty-one days are up. Dr. Ron Dougherty, the physician who runs the program, attempts to direct his patients to DEN and Argosy House for counseling or to methadone maintenance if he feels that they are unable to abstain from heroin use. Other agencies running abstinence programs use the detoxification unit to bring their clients "down" from heroin. Methadone maintenance was the last program to be brought into this narcotics establishment, and it will be described in the following chapters.

After the methadone clinic opened in 1971, another program developed outside this establishment as an aftercare center for methadone patients, Project RESCUE. It was promised aid from the OEO-supported Model Cities Program; however, it became embroiled in narcotics politics as it became the focus of much of this community's concern with the issue of methadone maintenance, and it was not supported (see Chapter V). In addition to the rehabilitation programs, in 1971 the county had matching state funds for a $3.9 million drug-prevention program in the schools administered by the Board of Cooperative Educational Services (BOCES). The network of drug programs and their links to state and local governments are illustrated in Table 4.

The relative sizes of the various rehabilitation programs in Syracuse are compared in Tables 5 and 6. An increasing percentage of the budget is going to methadone maintenance, but this involves no matching funds from the county.

Table 4.   Drug programs in Syracuse, 1971°

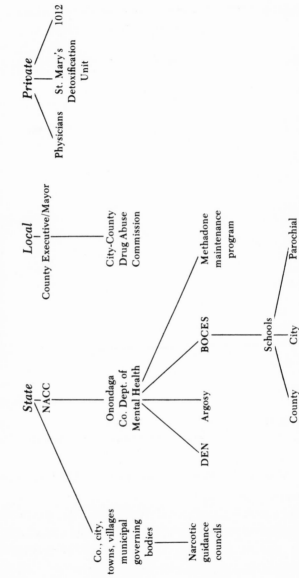

°*Source:* Adapted from Michael Reagen, ed., "Ideas about Drug Abuse: Proceedings from the Institute for Drug Education at Syracuse" Continuing Education Center, Syracuse University, 1971, (mimeograph).

Table 5. Utilization of services in addict rehabilitation
programs in Syracuse, 1971

Agency	Clients 1/1/71	Admissions	Terminations	Clients 1/1/72
DEN	46	169 (56 re-admissions)	146*	43
Argosy House Residence	21	38 (1 read-mission)	43 (3 graduates)	16
Day care**	19	129	129	19
Methadone maintenance program (began 4/71)	-0-	70	17	53
St. Mary's detoxification unit (began 2/71)	-0-	139 (19 read-missions)	131 (61 con-sidered "not using"—includes 23 on methadone)	8
1012	Logbook records 3000 + situations in 1971			

*DEN referred 26 clients to the methadone maintenance program at St. Joseph's Hospital.
**Argosy Argosy House records only those who participate in day care on a regular, ongoing basis.
More than one hundred individuals have been seen at the storefront for information and counseling.
Source. Data from Onondaga County Department of Mental Health.

As the number of programs increased, coordination among them became desirable. Dr. Dougherty, beginning his detoxification program in February 1971, invited representatives from other programs to meet at St. Mary's Hospital. Since then, every Thursday morning a group of twenty to thirty people dedicated to addict rehabilitation meet to discuss the progress of particular patients, their legal problems, family situations, and their response to treatment. This information facilitates the work of the various agencies; it helps to

Table 6.   Budgets of addict rehabilitation programs
in Syracuse, 1971 and 1972

	Budgets in 1971			
Program	*Net budget*	*Actual expenditures* 12/31/71	*Source of funds*	
Argosy House	$150,942	$79,140	NACC	$39,570
			County tax	19,570*
			Social services	21,477*
			Private	20,000
DEN	73,477	70,505	NACC	35,253
			County tax	30,452
			Private	4,800
Methadone maintenance	96,111	70,326	NACC	62,995
			Medicaid	7,331

*Not included in net budget amount.

place patients in programs appropriate to their needs
and to control those who try to bounce from one
rehabilitation service to another. The group includes
social workers, probation officers, nurses, and representatives from various rehabilitation programs. Few
doctors are involved, for out of about 630 M.D.'s in
Syracuse, only five have shown a sustained interest in
the problems of the addict.

When this group tries to match patients to programs,
the ideological differences among various therapeutic
approaches are evident. Both DEN and Argosy House
—the established narcotics treatment groups—are committed to total abstinence and are highly skeptical of
methadone maintenance. They are also irritated by the

Table 6. (continued)

Budgets in 1972

	Net budget	Projected source of funds	
Argosy House	$156,919	NACC	$81,960
		County	74,959
		Social services	51,360
		Private	23,500
DEN	77,804	NACC	48,124
		County	34,124
		Private	4,800
1012	49,000	NACC	36,000
		Private	13,000
Methadone maintenance 4/1/72-3/31/73	180,000 (req.)	NACC	180,000
		Medicaid & fees	20,000

Source: Data from Onondaga County Department of Mental Health, 1971.

professionalism involved in a medically-based treatment. The earliest programs in Syracuse were run by former addicts with considerable personal experience with drugs. A clinic run by professionals was threatening; "How can they have any idea of what it is like to be an addict?" They also fear that the methadone from the clinic may be diverted to illegal use. "Why don't you keep her methadone in a locker at the Syracuse bus terminal?" And they regard the program as spoonfeeding addicts who are unwilling to face up to their problems: "I got off it, why can't they?" They do not regard methadone as a solution, but as a "last resort," "the end of the road," "an admission of failure." Thus, while Henry Jackson, the director of DEN, refers addicts to the methadone program, he does so as the lesser of two evils, and only if they do not respond first to DEN's approach. And an Argosy director compared methadone to the former use of opium in China—"to shut 'em up and reduce the crime rate."

NOTES

[1]*Syracuse Herald-Journal*, November 10, 1971.

[2]*Syracuse Post-Standard*, November 11, 1971.

[3]*Syracuse Herald-Journal*, November 11, 1971.

[4]*Syracuse Post-Standard*, November 11, 1971. Widespread heroin use among middle-class teenagers is recent. A survey by the Toronto Addiction Research Center among children in grades seven to thirteen found that the rate of heroin use doubled between 1968 and 1970, with the highest rate of increase among children of professionals.

[5]*Syracuse Post-Standard*, November 11, 1971.

[6]A similar process is analyzed in Joseph Eaton, *Stone Walls Not a Prison Make* (Springfield: Charles C. Thomas, 1972), pp. 40–42. See also Ralph H. Turner, "Collective Behavior," in Robert Faris, ed., *Handbook of Modern Sociology* (Chicago: Rand McNally, 1964), pp. 382–425.

[7]Allen Campbell, *The Negro in Syracuse* (Syracuse: Syracuse University Press, 1964), pp. 1, 25.

[8]In 1969 the average weekly wage in Syracuse was $139.00, as compared to the national average of $130.00. Syracuse employment office, personal communication.

[9]In 1960 the Negro income was 77.6 percent of the white income. Campbell, *op. cit.*, p. 10.

[10]Syracuse-Onondaga County Planning Agency, *Job Accessibility: A Study of Factors Inhibiting Employment* (Syracuse, N.Y.: September 1969). See also Claire Rudolph, "Black Progress in Syracuse: 1960–1970," *Syracuse Metropolitan Review*, 3 (May 1970), 3–4.

[11]Allen Campbell, quoted in *New York Times*, August 11, 1971.

[12]Interview with Police Chief Thomas Sardino in Syracuse, *Metropolitan*

Review, 3 (April 1970), 1ff. A bag of heroin in Syracuse usually costs from six to ten dollars, depending on the supply. Assuming an addict uses five to six bags a day at an average cost of eight dollars, he would have to support a habit costing $17,000 annually.

[13]A detailed analysis of the Syracuse police force can be found in David M. Rafley, Edward A. Thibault, and Lawrence Lynch, "Race Labeling and Attitude; The Case of the Lake City Police" (unpublished manuscript based on a police survey in Syracuse). The police are poorly organized to deal with social problems in the black community. Most men in the Syracuse police force have lived in the Syracuse area for at least twenty-one years, that is, prior to the changes in the inner-city population. The force itself has only six black policemen, and a federally-funded community service aid project intended to recruit more blacks into the system has been delayed, because, it is said, of lack of cooperation from the black community. *Syracuse Herald-Journal*, October 18, 1971. The police, however, are highly sensitive to the race relations issue. The poll suggested that 64.3 percent perceived the Negro protest movement as violent rather than peaceful; 69.3 percent disapproved of actions taken by blacks to obtain civil rights; and 61.2 percent thought they were asking for too much. While most respondants indicated that more time should be spent working with members of the black community, those who worked in the field in potentially dangerous situations tended to dislike blacks, a resentment which fed on their own frustrations and sense of alienation.

[14]Thomas Sardino, "Parents Know the Drug Threat," article no. 12 of a series of articles reprinted from the *Syracuse Herald-Journal* throughout 1971. Sardino is known as the first police chief who was born in Syracuse. Previous chiefs included Pat Murphy and H.T. Smith, both of whom came from New York and left the Syracuse position to become New York City Chief of Police and first Deputy Commissioner respectively. The story goes that just as the Syracuse Chiefs are the farm team for the New York Yankees, so the Syracuse police chiefs are the farm club for New York City's police department.

[15]Personal interview with Sidney Joffe, October 1971.

[16]Roscoe C. Martin *et al.*, *Decisions in Syracuse*, Metropolitan Action Studies, No. 1 (Bloomington: Indiana University Press, 1961), Chap. 6.

[17]Syracuse has no visible cohesive organization of Muslims or Panthers or any other militant group within the black community.

IV / *The Organization of a Methadone Program*

The Onondaga County Department of Mental Health started the methadone maintenance program in a climate of urgency tempered by the ambivalence of other rehabilitation institutions, the police, and various community services. It was intended to broaden the type of treatment available to addicts and thus to help those not yet participating in existing programs. But a new program in a community represents a reallocation of scarce resources among new and existing interests. Careers and reputations are at stake.[1] Those who run other programs risk losing support if the new program succeeds; those sponsoring a new and controversial program risk loss of reputation if it fails. These attitudes affected all aspects of the Syracuse methadone maintenance program, from its initial funding and implementation to the eventual reception of its patients in the community.

Plans and Protocols

The Department of Mental Health initiated the methadone maintenance program with the stated purpose of allowing patients "to become free of the necessity of seeking money to purchase heroin on an undependable market, at an unpredictable dosage, at high personal risk, and with a great deal of total personal involvement which prevents them from participating in an ordinary way in the society of which they are a part."[2]

To set up such a program based on the controlled administration of an addictive drug required a four-level interaction among the County Department of Mental Health, a private hospital, and both state and federal bureaucracies. Donald Boudreau, head of the Department of Mental Health and coordinator of drug rehabilitation services, had to clear the proposal with the county legislature, negotiate with the hospital, apply for funds through the NACC, and acquire permits from the New York State Bureau of Narcotics Control, the New York State Department of Health, the Federal Food and Drug Administration, and the Internal Revenue Service. The process, required for all methadone programs, nearly smothered plans for the clinic in red tape. Problems of coordination were compounded by vague guidelines concerning application procedures and requirements, difficulty in mobilizing the hospital administration, and an uncertain funding situation.

The political use of the drug issue in the 1970 gubernatorial campaign had led to high expectations of state support. Responding to the encouragement of

Rayburn Hesse in early 1970, Dr. Boudreau began to explore possible locations for a methadone maintenance program. St. Joseph's Hospital was finally selected because of its existing contacts with the Department of Mental Health and the interest of Dr. Robert E. Pittenger, head of Psychiatric Services. St. Joseph's is a Roman Catholic hospital founded in 1869 by the Franciscan Sisters of the Third Order. In 1969 it had a bed capacity of 388, a well-staffed social service department, and 200 attending physicians. Hospital policy has encouraged new social service programs, requests for which are reviewed by a medical staff executive committee, on the assumption that new programs will depend eventually on hospital back-up services. Existing programs include the most extensive outpatient clinic in Syracuse, involving 41,779 patients. In 1964 the hospital added a twenty-patient psychiatric day-care unit, which was proposed as the setting of the methadone program.

Although St. Joseph's was the logical location for the new methadone program, hospital psychiatric services were already overburdened and understaffed, and the hospital administration hesitated to use these scarce resources, especially for a program not fully accepted by the medical community. Furthermore, the staff viewed addicts as considerably different from psychiatric patients and they were reluctant to take on the responsibility. In April 1970, however, the administration agreed to house the program.

Dr. Boudreau submitted application to the NACC for $162,000 for the remainder of the fiscal year ending March 31, 1971 (See Table 7).

Table 7.   Syracuse methadone maintenance program:
Application and accreditation procedures

1970

March	Boudreau discusses possibilities of methadone maintenance program with St. Joseph's Hospital and Dr. Pittenger.
April	Boudreau submits application for accreditation of the methadone program to the NACC for $162,000 for fiscal year ending March 31, 1971. Announces plans to seek local and state approval.
June	Negotiations between the county Department of Mental Health and St. Joseph's Hospital.
August 25	Health Committee of Onondaga County Legislature approves proposal and provides a $25,000 loan to initiate a program.
September 10	NACC approves county application and funded $99,523 from September 1, 1970 to March 31, 1971. Accreditation given through August 31, 1972.
September 10	County legislature unanimously approves program.
September 15	Request for FDA forms and approval procedures. Request for approval procedures from Internal Revenue Service. St. Joseph's Hospital is informed of application procedures and FDA forms are sent to the hospital.
September 22	Application for certification and registration is sent to New York State Bureau of Narcotics Control.
September	Negotiations concerning required laboratory support.
October 1	Intended opening date.
October 16	State Department of Health application is sent to St. Joseph's Hospital.
December 24	County Department of Mental Health fills out FDA form when it is realized that hospital had not yet done so.

1971

January 5	St. Joseph's sends a note to the FDA requesting an Investigational New Drug (IND) permit in order to obtain methadone and to initiate clinical study.
January 8	New York State Department of Health certificate #2563 is signed approving the Syracuse methadone program as a class V program.

(continued)

Table 7.   (continued)

February	Internal Revenue Service tax stamp received.
February 18	Following a reminder letter from the Department of Mental Health, St. Joseph's submits State Department of Health application.
February 19	An IND number, 7567, is received from the FDA indicating approval.
March 16	Approval from State Department of Health for operation under provision of the New York State Hospital Code.
April	Request to NACC for budget renewal.
June 9	Program officially opens.
June 22	Revised budget submitted to NACC for $100,000. NACC asks for further budget revision.
July 17	Request to NACC for new contract of $50,000 for July 1–December 31, 1971.
August	Application to the Division of Health Economics of the state Department of Health for a Medicaid rate.
October	Medicaid rate of $6.32 per visit received.
November	Funds received from NACC through December 1971.
January 1972	NACC approval for 1972, but funding delayed.

In September 1970 the NACC provided funding prorated at $99,523 for the period between September 1, 1970 and March 31, 1971. The budget, intended to serve one hundred patients, provided salaries for seven staff members—a social worker, two registered nurses, a rehabilitation counselor, two research assistants, and a receptionist—and one-fifth of the salaries of a psychiatrist, an internist, and an administrator. Equipment costs and laboratory fees were also included. Before the available funds could be used, however, both the Department of Mental Health and the hospital required permits, and the mass of complex paper work created considerable confusion. It was March 1971 before accreditation was complete; the program could not begin to use its NACC funding until only five days before the termination of its contract. The program quickly spent $13,000 on equipment; the balance had to be returned to the state.

Meanwhile, on the expectation of contract renewal, Dr. Pittenger unofficially began to accept a few patients in April 1971. By this time the NACC had overcommitted its funds, and in August 1971, after several months of negotiation, the NACC decided to contract the program for only $50,000 through December 1971.[3] Under this budget, the working staff of the program was headed by Dr. Pittenger as medical director and by an administrator with a background in nursing who had previously worked with Dr. Pittenger in Psychiatric Services at the hospital. Each worked part-time on the program and shared responsibility for program policy. A rehabilitation counselor with background in vocational guidance was hired to advise the patients on employment, housing, and other problems, and to place them in training programs or jobs in the community. The program also hired, at this time, two nurses and a receptionist to handle the daily clinic routine, and a research assistant, a former addict, who worked directly with the patients. Because the budget no longer allowed for a social worker, the second research assistant, or the services of an internist, the possibility of ancillary services was reduced; a patient needing medical help was simply referred to the hospital.

By October the NACC had still not signed the promised contract, a delay which gave rise to several rumors: that local political interests representing the pushers were interfering with funding,[4] that the legislature had gotten the political mileage it sought from the initial public announcement of the program and was no longer interested in exerting pressure to bring in funding, and that the NACC was favoring New York City programs at the expense of upstate New York. In the meantime the program was expanding, supported temporarily by the hospital and Medicaid rates, set at $6.32 per clinic visit. By November, when the contract was actually signed, the program was well under way, treating forty-five patients.

The initial plan had been to provide new inpatient psychiatric services and a residential program for addicts who had no job, family, or adequate living quarters. The reduced budget made these services out of the question; instead, the program was included, at first, in St. Joseph's psychiatric day-care clinic. Several patients who were admitted to the methadone program prior to its official opening came to this clinic. However, the association with the psychiatric clinic was quickly abandoned in response to objections from both the staff and the patients.

Months before the program was brought into the hospital, Dr. Pittenger had discussed the plans with the staff of Psychiatric Services. Yet at the last moment there remained serious objections. Nurses claimed the decision had been made without adequate consultation. In part, their objections were based on concerns common within hospitals over the distribution of authority and control. Hospital decision-making tends to be highly centralized, and nursing staffs, responsible for implementing programs on a day-to-day basis, often resent the authority of physicians and administrators. Nurses argued that the style of the psychiatric ward, based on trust, was inappropriate for addicts, who were accustomed to living by their wits and manipulating their environment; they would disrupt the daily routine.

The situation in this case was further complicated by stereotyped fears concerning addicts, who were believed to be "all psychopaths," violent, and likely to commit assault.[5] Husbands of several nurses forbade their wives to work in the clinic if it admitted addicts. Nurses denied that racial factors were involved in their reluctance to participate, but the situation was a new experience for most of them. Because of its Catholic affiliation and its location in a middle-income white neighborhood, St. Joseph's patients had been by and large middle-income people of Irish and Italian origin. Addicts themselves resented being placed with psychiatric patients; they differentiated between their own "voluntary addiction" and mental illness.

The combined attitudes of both patients and hospital staff resulted in a revised protocol which eliminated the inpatient phase except in the case of those who needed regular hospital care for medical reasons. Later, the methadone maintenance program moved to a separate facility across the street from the hospital, and it now has its own staff and no contact with psychiatric patients. Psychiatric services, if needed, were to be part of the methadone program, distinct from the regular hospital services.

When the plan to use a separate building was announced, the neighborhood was concerned about bringing addicts to the area. The hospital administration received several phone calls, one from a resident who requested that the hospital buy his house. But the hospital administration reassured the community, and the clinic quietly opened its doors on June 9, 1971.

The Patients

Requirements for admission to the methadone maintenance program assume, in the words of one of the program's administrators, that methadone is a "last resort."[6] Patients must be willing to involve themselves voluntarily in the program, which is open to both males and females of, in most instances, at least twenty-one years of age. Eighteen-year-olds are admitted if they meet the requirements of at least three years of heroin abuse and several prior attempts to abstain from drugs. Applicants who do not reside in the county are rejected, regardless of whether they meet the other requirements. In one case, an out-of-town addict asked if he could meet the residence requirement by leaving his clothes at a local church; he was refused. Finally, to be admitted, a patient must not have a serious mental illness, nor can he be a multiple-drug user.[7] The decision to accept or reject an applicant is made by the director following interviews by staff members. About 20 percent of those who applied were rejected because they had not been addicted long enough, or because they had never tried to "kick their habit" in other ways.

Who actually comes to the methadone maintenance program? In the first nine months of operation a total of seventy-one persons were actually admitted, though there were never more than fifty-four in the program at any one time. There are older patients who are tired of a life of hustling; there are those who are ill or those whose habit is too large to maintain, and who are desperate for a period of relief and time to pull themselves together. Some come under family pressure, others under pressure from the police. Although the program is voluntary, its clients have limited alternatives: if not methadone, it is prison, perpetual stealing to buy heroin, and the continual dread of arrest. The fact that welfare is not available to known addicts unless they are involved in a rehabilitation program brings people to the program as do "drug panics," when heroin is either unavailable or very expensive. The program accepts referrals from social, medical, and law enforcement agencies. The courts and the police do not generally refer patients to the program, but in several cases judges have agreed to put an addict on methadone instead of sending him to jail. Of the seventy-one persons admitted to the program, nine were awaiting trial and were offered conditional discharge if they entered a program, nine were on probation, and two were on parole when they applied. Thus some patients come to the program in order to avoid court action or to increase the possibility of a favorable judgment by a court or probation officer. In many cases, the addict simply walks off the street into the clinic.

The methadone clinic was not immediately deluged with applications. Six people were already involved when the program officially opened in June; enrollment increased as follows: June, 13; July, 25; August, 34; September, 51; October, 49; November, 52; December, 54. Life is less difficult for addicts in Syracuse than in larger cities. According to one addict, "It's very easy to meet a connection. . . . You don't have to know where to go. You can get off a bus and within a matter of minutes be there if you have money in your hand." Many addicts feel they are their own masters and that they can control their habits. The opposition of DEN, the group with the most contact among addicts, may also have affected applications. DEN considered application to the program as an admission of an addict's failure to find any reasonable solution to his problem; only in a desperate case was the risk worthwhile.[8]

Because Syracuse is a relatively small city, most addicts know each other, and this has significant influence on who decides to come to the program. Of the first group of forty-five patients, fourteen had heard of the program through a friend or a relative, and, in at least five of these cases, the friend was the former-addict research assistant working with the methadone program. Two others heard about the program on the street and just walked in. Two were referred by the Department of Mental Health; five came through referrals from hospitals or the neighborhood clinic; six came from DEN; and thirteen from the NACC. (No information was available on three patients.)

The first forty-five patients admitted to the program ranged in age from eighteen years old to forty-nine, distributed as in Table 8.

The average age of these first forty-five applicants was

Table 8:   Syracuse methadone maintenance program:
Age of patients, November 1971

Age	Number of patients
under 21	3 (youngest 18)
21-25	13
26-30	10
31-35	9
over 35	10 (oldest 49)

29.3 years. The average number of years of addiction was 8.9, ranging from as little as one year to as many as twenty-five. Thirty-seven were black and fifteen were women. Fifteen of the patients were married, including four married couples who came to the program together. Of the others, ten reported themselves as divorced or separated, the rest as single. Forty of the patients reported that they had been arrested: eighteen from one to five times; fourteen from six to ten times; and eight more than ten times. The average number of arrests for all patients was about seven. Though the demands of their habit had led most of the addicts to a similar life style, their backgrounds were diverse. Four of the patients had some college education, twelve others had finished high school, and another twelve had dropped out of the eleventh grade. Only one person had not completed eighth grade. Over half had never worked at any time in their lives, others had had temporary menial jobs; five had permanent jobs: a musician, a teacher, and a nurse were included among these.

The heroin habit for these patients ranged from one

bag a day to an alleged twenty-three, a bag containing about 100 milligrams of material which is from 5 to 10 percent pure heroin. The average habit was about six or seven bags daily. Only nine patients reported no previous connection with other established drug-abuse programs in town. Twenty-two had been associated with DEN, and eighteen had been at one time connected with the NACC criminal or civil commitment program. In each case, they had failed to stay drug free. Needing a respite, they saw in the methadone maintenance program a means to buy time: "It will give me a chance to get my head straight." Patients enter the program with the hope of getting themselves off drugs entirely once they "get straightened out." Relieved at first to be freed of hustling, as soon as they are stabilized on methadone and feel healthy, they think about getting detoxified and leaving the program.[9]

Procedures

Despite the needs that bring addicts to the methadone program, they have significant problems in adapting to its procedures and demands. An addict must take methadone every twenty-four hours to avoid withdrawal symptoms. Because of the potential for abuse of the drug, the Syracuse program, like others, requires that the patient swallow the methadone in the presence of a nurse, at least during the early part of treatment. Indeed, the need for staff control has been a major factor in shaping the formal structure of the program.

Each day the patient comes to the clinic located on the

first floor of a two-story frame house. He enters a small waiting room separated from a dispensing room by a locked Dutch door. To the right are small staff offices, and there is a single bathroom and a double-locked closet for the methadone. The clinic is open from 9:00 A.M. to 10:30 A.M. and from 2:30 P.M. to 4:30 P.M. every day, with some flexibility for those unable to meet these hours. On weekends it is open several hours in the morning.

At 8:30 A.M., before the clinic opens, a staff nurse goes to the hospital pharmacy, where the methadone is stored and prepared. She picks up the daily clinic supply as requested the day before. During the first five months of the program, methadone came in a powdered form already measured by the hospital pharmacist in correct doses for each patient and mixed with Tang in unbreakable plastic four-ounce baby bottles.[10] In October, to relieve the pharmacist of the burden of mixing the solution, the program began to order the methadone powder in sealed vials, each containing the appropriate dose for a particular patient. It is mixed with Tang at the clinic and the patients must drink it immediately in the presence of a nurse to assure that it is not sold or illegally distributed.

Most patients arrive early, when the clinic first opens. As in a bakery, each person takes a number when he arrives and waits his turn. Regardless of the number of staff members on duty, patients can only be given methadone one at a time, for, as a part of the procedure, each person must provide his urine sample in the presence of a nurse, and there is but one bathroom.

During the first stage of his participation in the program, an addict begins medication at a level compatible with his habit, and this is steadily increased to a regular dose of approximately 100 milligrams per day. He will reach his stable dose of methadone in about six weeks, after which he must continue to come to the clinic each day for personal and vocational counseling until he is socially stabilized to the point of "being gainfully employed and self-supporting, his living situation adequate and orderly, and family relationships in most instances positive and emotionally satisfying."[11] At first, attendance at therapy groups was also mandatory, but patients were reluctant to participate. It was soon made voluntary, and relatively few continued to come.

The frequency of required visits to the clinic is reduced at the discretion of the program director, on the basis of the following guidelines: after thirteen weeks "clean," that is, with no urine positives which indicate that a patient has taken heroin or another narcotic, he may take methadone home on weekends. After seventeen weeks clean, he must come to the clinic only three times weekly; after twenty-two weeks, only twice weekly.[12] Some patients must participate in therapy groups if they are to take methadone home.

The analysis of urine samples is clearly a crucial part of the program, for it serves as a check on the presence of heroin, amphetamines, or barbiturates. Until December 1971 the analysis procedure was not able to detect cocaine, a common street narcotic, but the quinine with which cocaine and other drugs are often cut is detectable. The analysis is a complex procedure requiring sensitive equipment which can distinguish morphine from other narcotics by a thin-layer chromatographic procedure.[13] It requires a system which can screen large numbers of specimens rapidly and an organization which can get the results back to the clinic promptly. St. Joseph's negotiated with several laboratories to analyze the samples. They could not contract with the first because its procedures seemed unnecessarily complicated. They made temporary arrangements with a California firm which proved unreliable;[14] in any case, the firm took six weeks to provide a sample analysis. They finally signed a contract with a Buffalo firm: the hospital pays $3.31 for each specimen, a price including containers, transportation via Greyhound, and telephone reporting. Specimens are sent from Syracuse every Monday, Wednesday, and Friday by Greyhound; the laboratory phones in reports of positives the next afternoon and mails a written report on all samples received within two days. This system, required by law, permits an up-to-date check on the response of the patients to the program.

Rules and Their Implementation

The above procedures follow the general guidelines provided by the Beth-Israel Medical Center outpatient program (see Chapter II). The implementation of these procedures reflects the objectives and concerns of the clinic staff. Decisions ultimately rest with Dr. Pittenger, the medical director of the program, but with only one-fifth of his time allotted to the clinic, and with a major responsibility as head of psychiatric services for St. Joseph's Hospital, he depends heavily on the program administrator. Since she too is part time, the day-to-day functioning of the clinic as it most directly affects the clients is in the hands of the full-time members of the staff. They feel a stake in the success of the program, and "success" is inevitably interpreted in terms of the response of patients. Yet the definition of success is controversial, and various staff members have very different views. These differences are evident in their ideas about how strictly or leniently the clinic should be run. Some think that the program is not sufficiently firm in stating and implementing rules, while others take the position that procedures should be flexible enough to accommodate the needs of individual patients.

At first there were no rules and patients were simply told the procedures. The medical director felt that rules were necessary to guide the staff but that one must always ask, "What do the rules cost the individual?" Claiming that patients would follow rules only because they were afraid to jeopardize their position, he preferred to be lenient, allowing mistakes, adjusting to patients' life styles and expectations. However, one staff member called Dr. Pittenger "a marshmallow" and, along with several others, insisted that rules must be clearly drawn. In August 1971 the staff made an abortive effort to formalize the procedures by strictly defining the limits of appropriate behavior at the clinic in a set of rules:

Do not engage in anti-social behavior. The following activities shall be considered anti-social behavior: abuse of drugs, excessive use of alcohol, threat to or assault upon any individual, conviction of crime, abusive language to staff.

The rules went on to specify that patients must submit to physical and laboratory tests, relay information regarding physical condition when asked to do so, take no other drugs without authorization, make sincere efforts to find employment, call the clinic if delayed, and respect the fact that clinic premises are restricted to participants in the program. Finally, the rules concluded with a warning in capital letters that "Violation of any one or a combination of the above regulations may be used as cause for being dropped from the program upon decision of the clinic staff."

It is hardly surprising that patients objected to these rules as insulting and paternalistic. Some staff members also were concerned, and the list was withdrawn. For the moment, no further rules were distributed; later revisions omitted the list of antisocial behaviors and added a note that "this is not a final or fixed document, and suggestions from patients and/or staff will be considered for additions or changes."

The pressure to enforce rules continued, however. "Of what use are rules if they are broken all the time?" asked one of the nurses. This attitude reflected two concerns of the staff; they hoped that rules would minimize manipulation by patients, and they felt it in the best interest of patients to have a clearly defined structure in the program. Most of the staff felt that addicts, like children, are better off within a well-

defined situation in which they are forced to make
choices and to take responsibility for their own behavior.
But also the staff felt threatened by a loose interpretation of the rules. If rules could be bent, their authority
could be undermined. The first head nurse left the
program after three months because he felt he was
forced to "mollycoddle joyriders." He claimed that with
few rules and limited possibilities of staff control,
patients take advantage; he felt manipulated. Finally,
the staff was concerned with the public image of the
program. For example, the program administrator,
faced with practical problems of funding, saw the need
for increased strictness and control in order to protect
against what outsiders might consider failure. The
tenuous status of the program and its limited resources
fostered a demand for visible evidence of order and
short-term success, although, as in the case of the
unfortunate set of rules, this could undermine the
broader goals of the program.

To some extent, the concern with leniency and
authority within the program reflected the classic
conflict between those staff members immediately
responsible for daily routines and those with administrative authority. Nurses must cope with the daily demands
of patients, and, in addition, they are caught between
two lines of authority—administrative and medical. This
kind of conflict is particularly evident in a program such
as methadone maintenance, where the boundaries
between clinical and administrative decisions are
nebulous. A decision interpreted by the physician as
requiring clinical authority may be interpreted by the

staff as an administrative matter. Often Dr. Pittenger's independent actions on what he felt to be clinical grounds were regarded as undermining staff authority.

Three aspects of the program have been a particular source of conflict in the enforcement of rules: the criteria for admission, the grounds for suspension, and the pressure put on addicts to find jobs. Whether to admit "difficult" patients has been the most controversial admissions question. For example, in deciding whether to admit a dealer as a patient, some staff members felt that he would merely use the program for operating his thriving business more effectively, while others argued that if he no longer had to support his habit he might stop pushing. In any case, the man had an enormous habit of twenty-five bags a day and sought help. He was eventually accepted when he "proved" his motivation by reducing his habit to eight bags a day prior to admission. Admissions decisions are also controversial when they concern persons under indictment. "Our goals are not to spring people from jail." Similarly, admission of multiple-drug users raises problems. Should the program limit itself to the easiest patients and assure itself of success in terms of the patients' eventual societal participation? Or, would it be more useful to take on difficult patients, and be satisfied with mitigating individual problems?

On the issue of criteria for suspension, some staff members argue for rigid rules, considering that forced adherence to well-defined rules is in the client's best interest. The question of suspension was brought to a point of decision with the appearance of quinine positives in the urine of many patients. In the fall of 1971 an increased supply of cocaine appeared in town, and it was usually cut with quinine. After several warnings, the staff laid down rules to the effect that it would consider the presence of quinine in the urine as evidence of cocaine use. "Use of cocaine is not consistent with the methadone program. The program is for individuals who want to get away from the use of illicit drugs. . . . If quinine continues to be found in the urine, the individual may be suspended or discharged."[15] Three positives became grounds for suspension, which means a seven-day detoxification period in which the addict is given declining doses of methadone until he is drug free. He then cannot reenter the program for twenty-three days. Regarded as a "therapeutic" measure, suspension is not reported to the narcotics authorities. On the other hand, threatening physical violence against the staff or other patients, selling or giving away methadone, or possession of an illicit drug are grounds for involuntary discharge, and the staff will report these as well as voluntary departures to state authorities.

Following the cocaine incidents, five people were suspended, and the appearance of quinine positives temporarily ceased. The staff have had mixed feelings about the suspension policy. Some supported it, convinced that a more permissive policy would encourage "freeloaders." "We don't want this program to be the Heroin Hilton." Others were uneasy, particularly in view of the fact that several of the suspended patients had scarcely been in the program long enough to lose their heroin hunger. They were also sympathetic to the difficulty addicts have in reorganizing their lives to meet the program's routine. In fact, as the program has continued, the number of suspensions has decreased. Total suspensions, departures, and discharges among the seventy-one patients admitted during the first nine months are as given in Table 9.

Table 9. Syracuse methadone maintenance program: suspensions, departures, and discharges by March 1, 1972

Suspensions (30 days)	Voluntary departure	Involuntary Discharges
4 stopped coming (not yet discharged)	7 requested detoxification	2 failed to comply with rules
3 for excessive absence	7 stopped coming— discharged	1 could not substantiate drug history
5 for continued drug use	5 failed to return following suspension	1 committed to mental hospital
	1 entered an abstinence program	1 for excessive absence
	1 left but was later readmitted	

Finally, questions of leniency arose over the demands placed on patients to find employment. When the rehabilitation counselor feels a patient is ready to work, she tries to find him a job through the State Office of Vocational Rehabilitation, the State Employment Service, and various minority hiring and training groups. In spite of her skill, her job is difficult: the stereotyped image of addicts as deviant and unable to work, the depressed state of the economy, and the small numbers of jobs for unskilled workers make it difficult to place addicts. Five patients were employed before they entered the program. By March 1, 1972, fourteen of the fifty-one persons in the program at that time were employed as shown in Table 10.

Table 10.   Syracuse methadone maintenance program:
Employment of patients, March 1972

3 *Musicians*
3 *Narcotics program aides*
1 *Theater production assistant*
1 *Teacher*
1 *Cab driver*
2 *Laborers*
1 *City recreation worker*
1 *Food service worker*
1 *Family retail business*

All of these persons had been in the program at least six months. Ten others had at some time been employed, usually in part-time jobs, and five had been in and out of jobs or training programs several times. There is, in other words, an enormous fluctuation.

Local businesses are reluctant to hire known addicts, and the State Employment Service, working for employers and not applicants, reflects community skepticism. However, by October 1972, energetic efforts to find employment for patients were beginning to show remarkable success. Of forty-five patients in the program at that time, twenty-six were employed full time, three were in training programs, and five were taking care of their children full time. But few employers knew that they were hiring methadone patients and those who found out have fired them. For example, a patient, forced by a scheduling adjustment to tell his boss he was on methadone, lost his job. The director of a minority training program feared that he would risk his own program by taking addicts from methadone maintenance, and the director of a nursing training program refused to accept a qualified patient into the program because she was still "addicted." In another case, a county department fired an employee when it learned that she was on methadone, apparently without realizing the irony involved in one county agency undermining the efforts of another and, by doing so, forcing a person onto county-funded work relief.

To compound these difficulties, addicts often have unrealistic ideas about jobs. A recent study attempting to identify the particular characteristics of those vulnerable to narcotics use indicated that prior to addiction the typical addict had higher aspirations and was more aggressive than others of similar backgrounds.[16] Those with high aspirations but few skills have problems finding jobs that satisfy them, and they often prefer to take no jobs at all. In addition, there are problems of reliability among people adjusted to "street time," whose schedule is dictated by the physical needs of their habit. The rehabilitation counselor, aware of the life-style adjustments involved, does not want to force people into employment. The program administrator, on the other hand, feels that patients should be forced to find a job within six months, that for their own good "we must force people to do something for themselves." Otherwise patients will say, "Why in hell should I go out and work when I can collect welfare?"

Those who seek to increase demands on patients see this as a means of forcing personal responsibility and independence upon the addict. Yet there is a dilemma: is it appropriate to turn the "lifeline" of methadone into an instrument of coercion, a means of controlling a person's behavior? And, considering the public stigmatization of the addict, and the options available to him, is it reasonable and realistic to define individual responsibility in terms of employment and full participation in society? After five months of operation, these problems became evident and the program's original statement of purpose was expanded by taking into account "the enormously complex stigmatization which addicts feel and experience from the community for having been addicted and having to continue to take medication for a prolonged period."[17]

NOTES

[1]The pattern of commitment to existing institutions is discussed in Lloyd E. Ohlin, "Conflicting Interests in Correctional Objectives," in Social Science Research Council, *Theoretical Studies in Social Organization of the Prison*

(New York, 1960), 111–129. See also Florence Heynman, "Methadone Maintenance as Law and Order," *Society*, 9 (June 1972), 16.

[2]Methadone Maintenance Program, "Purposes," April 1971 (mimeographed).

[3]This $50,000 plus the $13,000 from the previous allocation gave the program a budget of $63,000 plus Medicaid funds (see Table 5). During this period of negotiation, the local uncertainty was so intense that Dr. Boudreau requested Emil Drysdale, the director of NACC agency affairs, to send in writing an indication that there was no intention to terminate the Syracuse program.

[4]The program could have had, in fact, a sizable impact on the illegal drug market. If one hundred hard-core addicts with a habit of $50 per day were no longer to buy heroin, this would remove almost $2 million of annual trade from pushers.

[5]There is evidence that addicts fill the entire span of categories of psychiatric diagnosis proportionate to the nonaddict population. According to Marie Nyswander, M.D., "Addicts may be schizophrenic, obsessive-compulsive, hysteric, psychopathic, or have simple character disorders. Although once addicted, the behavior of all addicts may closely resemble each other (at least in the social sense of behavior), basically the individuals may be very different indeed." Quoted in Nat Hentoff, *A Doctor among the Addicts* (New York: Grove Press, Evergreen Black Cat ed., 1970), pp. 76–77. See also Alfred R. Lindesmith, *Addiction and Opiates* (Chicago: Aldine, 1968), pp. 157–172.

[6]*Syracuse Herald-Journal*, June 18, 1971.

[7]Admission rules have been waived in several cases: one case involved a delicate employment situation which required stabilization; others involved addict families in which both husband and wife were addicted.

[8]Daniel Glaser (personal communication) has pointed out a similar problem in New York City where a central referral service was set up to refer addicts on welfare to various treatment services. Former addicts from drug-free programs who serve as classifiers refuse to send anyone to methadone.

[9]Any patient who wants to be detoxified is helped by the clinic, since participation is voluntary. Eight people were detoxified on request, but four were back on methadone within a month.

[10]This form of bottling is required by the Bureau of Narcotics, for the reason that if a box of bottles is dropped, losing a large quantity of methadone, there would be considerable problems of accountability to federal auditors.

[11]Mimeographed protocol, "Revised Narrative—Methadone Maintenance Treatment Program," n.d., pp. 4–5.

[12]Rules require that any methadone allowed out of the clinic be transported in a locked box. Stolen or lost methadone cannot be replaced. Nevertheless there are continuing reports of accidental poisonings.

[13]Bernard Davidow *et al.*, "Thin Layer Chromatographic Screening Test for the Detection of Users of Morphine or Heroin," *American Journal of Clinical Pathology*, 46 (July 1966), 58–61.

[14]In a random check, a geriatric urine was identified as a heroin positive.

[15]From list of rules posted in the clinic. Grounds for suspension also include absence for four days without advanced authorization.

[16]Daniel Glaser, Bernard Lander, and William Abbott, "Opiate Addicted and Non-Addicted Siblings in a Slum Area," *Social Problems*, 18 (Spring 1971), 510–521. See also John Horton, "Time and Cool People," in *Trans-action*, 5 (April 1967), pp. 5–11.

[17]Methadone Maintenance Program, "Purposes," revised, August 6, 1971 (mimeographed).

V / *The Addict as Patient*

Problems of Adaptation

The addict responds to the demands of the methadone maintenance program in terms of his own objectives, which are to protect his relationship with a system he regards as a "lifeline," to adapt to its demands, and, at the same time, to retain his autonomy as much as possible. These objectives are complicated by the unique problems of being a methadone patient. For he is in a socially marginal category, a person who "having left one social group without making a satisfactory adjustment to another, finds himself on the margins of each but a member of neither."[1] Before entering the program he was dependent on narcotics, and defined and rejected by society as an addict. He comes from an addict subculture with its unique way of looking at the world, its own expectations, and a shared life style based on the need for heroin.[2] Only the doctor-addict, whose life is not dominated by the difficulty of obtaining drugs, is exempt from the pressures that form the subculture. Set apart from the larger society, the addict's identification is total, based on and reinforced by common need.

In a small city like Syracuse, most of the addicts live in the same neighborhood; those who live elsewhere use the same few sources to get their fix. Because the addict is isolated by the fact of the illegality of his daily pursuits, his ties to his friends serve primarily as protection against outsiders who may be plainclothesmen and against a time when he may be unable to get the money necessary to maintain his habit. Yet the addict also operates as an individual entrepreneur: no obligations can take precedence over supporting his habit.[3] Particular skills are required to support a habit, including the ability to "beat the system," to negotiate and to manipulate the environment, to keep cool, and to steal. Stealing is not perceived as wrong; it is simply necessary for survival and is the economic basis of street life.

The norms of regularity and dependability associated with employment and with scheduled obligations are irrelevant to the addict subculture. The addict's concept and rhythm of time is strictly personal; it is not adapted to a schedule set by society patterned by the day or by the week, but "to the chance and accidental character of events on the street"[4] and by the immediate demands of getting a fix to stave off withdrawal symptoms. Time is necessarily directed not to the future, but to present needs.

Once in the program, the addict is no longer dependent on street sources to meet the needs of his habit, but he is still dependent on a drug and socially defined as an addict. The program expects him to adapt fully to the norms and patterns of a drug-free life, yet his

physical dependence on methadone and his social status
as an addict make this extremely difficult to do. He is thus
in the position characteristic of the marginal person, a
position poorly defined, transitional, and filled with
uncertainty. All of the patients in the Syracuse program
remain in the same neighborhoods in which they were a
part of the addict subculture, but they now have a
changed relationship to their previous associates. No
longer involved in the social life which is oriented
around narcotics, they tend to be isolated. Nor do they
belong to the community of former addicts who are
active in DEN, for these look down on the still-addicted
methadone patients. Occasionally, some of the methadone patients will go to a social event at DEN, but they
report being "put down," and many hesitate to return.
There is some relief from isolation in the fact that most
of the black patients have known each other for a long
time, but this may also be a source of friction: for as
people find time to begin to assess and reorganize their
lives, they become increasingly aware of past debts and
hostilities. Couples on the methadone program have
particular problems, for often their relationships are tied
together by the need of mutual help in getting drugs.
Once the pressure is relieved, other strains become
more apparent, and several are having domestic
troubles.

Few patients have been in the program long enough
to have stabilized their family relationships. At one point
there were ten methadone mothers, with thirty-six
children, most of them living with grandmothers.
Methadone patients seem to remain unusually depend-

ent upon their parents, often through their own children, a situation which is difficult for many of them.

Conflicts also arise between old friends, although only once did hostility develop into a fight in the clinic. This fight, between two women, developed after a street incident in which one was arrested and the other denied being with her. The fight was immediately stopped by several male patients who feared the program would be jeopardized. Patients are careful to protect their "lifeline," and they find means of handling their problems privately. Apparently they also protect the clinic; while the hospital, directly across the street, has been vandalized several times, the methadone clinic has not been victim to such attacks.

Patients must adapt to program demands within this context of personal isolation. When an addict enters the program, he must first confront his fears about the side effects of methadone. These effects, such as increased constipation, sweating, and irregularity of the menstrual period (several women have been concerned that their blood would "back up"), are particularly evident during the first four to six weeks. Some physical symptoms are merely carry-overs from the patient's previous heroin addiction. For example, dental problems are common, the consequence of earlier neglect. Some patients worry that methadone addiction might be worse than the heroin habit, and withdrawal much harder. There are rumors that bones will dissolve. But concerns about unknown physical effects subside as the patients adjust physically to their drug dosage. Comparing notes with each other, most patients gradually come to accept the comparatively minor physical difficulties.

A more serious problem for many addicts is adapting to the new time scale. The methadone program forces the addict to adapt to a regular twenty-four-hour routine, while on heroin he had measured time by the few hours between one bag and the next. This demand in itself is a form of initiation into a society where high value is placed on maintaining a regular schedule. In addition, societal goals inherent in the program imply a future orientation, inconsistent with the addict's pattern of seeking immediate relief. The patient finds it hard to tolerate delay, and waiting his turn at the clinic is a source of continuing irritation. Yet, relieved of the necessity to hustle, he has no idea of what to do with his newly found freedom and excess time; boredom is a major source of anxiety. When the program was small, patients often came around to the clinic and talked to the staff and to each other. As the number of patients increased, this became difficult in the small physical quarters. Staff members complained that those who stayed around disrupted the routine. A request from patients to set up a card table in the waiting room was refused. To relieve their boredom, some patients continue to hustle, for new clothes and, in some cases, for drugs. Thus, boredom, combined with continued association with the old community, make it difficult for an addict to adapt fully to the expectations of a "normal" life.[5]

Finally, perhaps the most difficult adjustment for

many addicts entering the program is adapting to a rule-bound routine. The assumptions and expectations apparent in the program's statement of purpose (p. 95) are clearly extremely difficult for the addict to handle because they are in sharp contrast with the assumptions and expectations of his past life style.

Beating the System

For many heroin addicts, addiction is a way of defying authority, "the most tempting and the most rationalized of all revolts . . . a way of stating their independence."[6] Despite the needs that bring the addict to the methadone program, as patients they resist submitting to rules and procedures and seek means to control these procedures and so to maintain their autonomy. The staff, however, does not regard addicts as having sufficient ability or sense of responsibility to share in rule making. Staff members characterize addicts as "scheming and cunning," "like children," "unable to delay gratification." The distribution of methadone in baby bottles is an accidental but striking symbol.

Staff professionalism also fosters an authoritarian attitude, and the needs of patients to maintain autonomy in dealing with rules may conflict with what the staff perceives as necessary to run the program efficiently. "They have no concept that there are other things we have to do." Addicts have a tendency to test the system, and this reinforces the staff assumption that strictly defined rules formulated at the top and transmitted down are necessary. Yet this assumption conflicts with the mutual participation required to maintain a long-term medical relationship between the patient and the program.

Patients have sought participation in program policy in several ways. First, they requested that the program hire black nurses. The director tried to comply, but failed, for black nursing students, themselves upwardly mobile, were reluctant to work with addicts on a daily basis. Patients also tried to convince the staff to hire one of them as a research assistant. But hospital policy dictated that no patient could be hired by any program within a year of being discharged. To hire methadone patients would have involved a change in policy; a black college student with experience in a rehabilitation program in New York was employed instead.

Unable to influence policy directly, patients try to carve out areas of autonomy by manipulating the routine, particularly where the structure of authority is most evident. The primary symbol of control in the program is the requirement of a daily monitored urine sample, a routine which they accept as necessary but resent as an indignity and as evidence of mistrust. Also, new patients often have physical difficulty in urinating. The patients' distaste for the procedure is especially evident in the waiting room on weekends, when the clinic is only open for a short time and is relatively busy. Tension is sometimes expressed in humorous references to "the peeing cup" or to "picking a peeing number." Patients tease the staff: "Don't *you* forget to pee in the cup." Patients inspect their own urine, commenting if it is darker than usual. Worried about their general state of health, they often request to have the samples checked for medical problems. Sometimes, while in the bathroom, they will try to talk privately to the monitoring nurse about their health problems. With a line of people waiting, however, there is seldom time.

The patients have tried to beat this system by taking drugs which do not show in the urine. Since cocaine is mixed with quinine, quinine positives are an indication of "cheating." The cocaine itself, if taken in small quantities or snorted, breaks down faster than the quinine and does not show in a urinalysis. When quinine positives were first found in the urine of ten patients, the staff assumed that the quinine had been used to cut cocaine; patients argued that it was from gin and tonics. One even claimed that his mother had baked cookies with quinine. When rules were posted to the effect that quinine positives would automatically be considered evidence of narcotics or cocaine use, patients regarded this as unfair. The incidence of quinine positives (see Table 11) suggests the addicts' attempts to test the limits of the system. However, once threatened with suspension, few continued to jeopardize their place in the program.

Patients are also concerned that program authority dictates their dosage, and here they also try to manipulate the system. Patients are not supposed to know their dosage of methadone, and they resent this. One girl, for example, complained that she was feeling high and suspected that the nurse had increased her dose. She felt that her dosage was her business and that at the very least she should be informed so as to know

Table 11.   Syracuse methadone maintenance program:
Urine positives as evidence of narcotics use

Month	Number of positives	Drug	Number of people involved
	(total—639 urinalyses)		(total—51 patients)
Jan. 1972	3	Amphetamines	2
	12	Quinine	7
	8	Doriden	6
	1	Cocaine	1
	(total—689 urinalyses)		(total—51 patients)
Feb. 1972	3	Amphetamines	2
	43*	Quinines	11
	1	Morphine	1

*Three persons who had requested to go drug free and were in various stages of detoxification were responsible for thirty-five of the forty-three positives.

what to expect. For the first few months the amount of Tang was proportionate to the amount of methadone, and patients tried to calculate their dosage by comparing the total amount of liquid in their cups. Later, to avoid such comparisons, the staff filled all bottles to the same level. Nevertheless, patients continued to negotiate for more or less methadone on the basis of perceived side effects.

Finally, patients manipulate their relationship to the program by avoidance. Most, for example, will not participate in the therapy groups. Two groups were formed when the program began and patients were to join one of them and come regularly. One had a steady attendance of a core group of five to six older addicts who had been in the program since it began and felt comparatively secure. They used the therapy session as a social occasion or attempted to divert it to a critique of the program. The second group had no regular attendance. Patients regard therapy as irrelevant to their needs; one man described it as an attempt to "brainwash us with middle-class values which are of no use when we return to the ghetto." Dr. Pittenger explained the failure of the therapy groups: "The patients are afraid of the power of the staff. They feel that if they reveal how badly they are doing and how unhappy they are, or if they imply that the program is in some ways unsuccessful for them, they might be cut off."

The staff was sensitive to the patients concerns about therapy but continued to perceive the therapeutic process in traditional psychiatric terms. Perhaps the patients' desire to use clinic space for recreational purposes could have been made the basis of a therapeutic program, but there is no evidence that this was seriously considered. Instead, the staff responded to growing evidence of patient dissatisfaction by setting up a monthly "town meeting" in which various problems could be aired.

At first, few patients came to the town meetings, and those with the most complaints failed to appear at all. In August the staff tried to set up a representative patient council; a group was nominated at the town meeting, but there were immediate organizational difficulties. One aggressive person dominated and the others resented him, so the effort at representation was abandoned. In October only nine people attended the town meeting. By the next month, however, interest revived because of concern about the suspension procedures which had been established when the quinine positives were found. Twenty-seven out of the fifty-three patients in the program at this time attended the town meeting and elected six people to a new patients' council. On the one hand, patients were upset about the quinine positives, denying that cocaine was being widely used; on the other, they claimed that there were some addicts who intended to get suspended for thirty days in order to go on a shooting spree, knowing that they could get back into the program afterward. This was, they felt, a threat to the program and to themselves. The council wanted to know who was suspected of using drugs, for they wanted to regulate the problem of abuse themselves. This request presented several problems for the staff, who were concerned about the ethics of confidentiality, the dangers of peer pressure, and the development of a new power group within the patient community. The staff decided that the council could interview those patients who voluntarily agreed to be interviewed and those who reentered the program following a suspension. Furthermore, council interviews were to serve the purpose of support, not punishment or control.

A Self-Help Effort

The patients' desire to maintain independence and autonomy took expression when those who had been most active at the town meetings formed a controversial organization, Project RESCUE (Redemption, Education, Socialization, Communication, Understanding, and Employment).

In early 1971, John English, who had been an addict for twenty-three of his forty-one years and had been a patient at DEN, spent three weeks in the detoxification unit at St. Mary's hospital. During this period of imposed isolation, English thought a great deal about the needs of black addicts and why they return to drugs. He developed a plan for a club which he called Freedom. After detoxification, English went back on heroin and later became one of the first methadone patients in Syracuse. During his first summer on the program, he began to organize an arts and crafts rehabilitation group and interested about fifteen other black patients from the methadone program. English soon expanded his plan, proposing a neighborhood center to provide support and regular peer group therapy for former addicts living in the inner city where the conditions of poor housing, unemployment, and crime which had led them to addiction still existed. His idea was that methadone maintenance patients particularly needed such a center, for while methadone is useful in providing addicts time to reorganize their lives, it fails to help them with their social problems. He saw the need of a project to fill a void, to provide a social base for methadone patients who are isolated from their community and who find it difficult to settle into regular employment. By September, English wrote a proposal for Project RESCUE, a total rehabilitation program. The proposal was sent to the Model Cities Program and to the City Urban Crisis Fund to support a program "designed to help detoxify addicts, establish the necessary discipline and value system to cope with the problems that led to addiction."[8] The proposal sought support for vocational training, scholarships, an information center, and a crisis center called a "hot-line service."

Meanwhile English sought space for his small arts and crafts program and backing for his proposal, for Model Cities required an "umbrella agency" to back projects before support would be provided. Neither the methadone program nor St. Joseph's Hospital would provide such backing. However, English found a sympathetic sponsor at the YMCA, where he was employed on the maintenance crew. The Y provided a room for meetings and agreed to become an "umbrella." The director of the Y assisted English in his quest for project funds.

While he was waiting for a response to the proposal, English organized a small program in a single room at the YMCA. The room contained several desks and tables, a television set, a blackboard, and many bridge chairs. Posters decorated the walls, one entitled "black freedom," another with a picture of a syringe labeled "modern crucifixion." On a bulletin board were newspaper clippings with such titles as "Heroin can be deadly," and a sign on the blackboard read, "If you're not a part of the solution, then you're a part of the problem." The room served as a social center for twenty to thirty of the methadone patients who met there daily, sharing their concerns and filling in their leisure time. Participants refer to themselves as a big family: "We are all relatives." Every Sunday the addicts, their families, and friends attend a meeting with a religious focus. As with Alcoholics Anonymous, "spiritual reflection" is an important aspect: "People are encouraged to talk about their revelations without feeling uncomfortable . . . to seek inspiration and awakening. . . . The sessions make people feel good when they are over."[9] A participant in RESCUE noted that "once his health was back," he was bored and lonely and had too much time on his hands. RESCUE had given him something to do. Volunteers offered training in crafts and in typewriter and air-conditioning repair. Subgroups formed—one worked on training projects, another moved out to the community, seeking promises for employment and support for "scholarships." English also organized a chicken barbecue to raise money for the program, and managed to talk Colonel Sanders into donating free chickens.

When Model Cities indicated that they might fund Project RESCUE and it became apparent that it would be more than just an arts and crafts workshop, English's activities became highly controversial. Every existing drug agency in town opposed RESCUE, and when English asked to be included in the Thursday meetings of all those working on addict rehabilitation, he was turned down. Henry Jackson from DEN was the most vocal opponent. English, he argued, was neither reliable nor competent, and his program was all plans and no action. "We don't need more rhetoric in the community." Moreover, he claimed that English was only duplicating existing efforts. The source of Jackson's opposition was rooted in an old personal feud between these two highly competitive and independent personalities. English had once so strongly opposed DEN policy that Jackson had suspended him from the program. Now RESCUE, working with patients, some of whom had once been in DEN and had returned to drugs, represented a personal challenge as well as potential competition for scarce rehabilitation resources.

Jackson claimed that the methadone maintenance program had "created a monster by encouraging English." But the methadone staff denied having done so, and fluctuated between amazement at English's success in developing the program and discomfort about his activities with their clients—for English had involved more than half of the methadone patients. He had hoped to gain the open collaboration of the methadone program and to have them regard RESCUE as an extension or outreach service; but the methadone program relied on referrals and contacts with DEN, and to support John English would have seemed a direct affront to Henry Jackson. Furthermore, methadone staff members felt that they were being used as political leverage to help RESCUE get funding, and just at the sensitive period when the program itself had considerable funding troubles. The staff also believed that English's promises of training and employment were raising false expectations which could not be met. They feared that he would divert patients from seeking other jobs, setting back the methadone program's own rehabilitation efforts. Finally, the staff decided to give English moral support but to encourage him to start on a smaller scale than he had planned, for they watched the widening scope of his project with concern.

Similarly, the Department of Mental Health and the City-County Drug Commission, which had to endorse the project before funding could be approved, was concerned with its scope. Dr. Boudreau wrote a supportive letter, but recommended that the program focus more narrowly on a sheltered-workshop model. Pressured by Boudreau's recommendation, the commission, after considerable internal controversy, reluctantly supported the program with the qualifications suggested by Boudreau.

By November, RESCUE was facing serious consequences from its opposition. Funding for three months was tentatively approved by the Model Cities Program at $40,000, about one-third of what was requested. (The request to the Urban Crisis Fund was refused.) Use of the grant was still contingent on the Y acting as "umbrella agency." But at this time, the board at the YMCA was besieged with complaints from rehabilitation programs, from law enforcement agencies, and from community groups, reminding the board that its formal responsibility was to work with teenagers and that the involvement with RESCUE was beyond its mandate. Rehabilitation of addicts was the responsibility of other agencies. The board of the Y, which included two judges and the director of Argosy House, decided that it could no longer back the program. The YMCA director helped English to look for another "umbrella," but again all existing agencies refused and without such backing RESCUE could not use its funding. On November 1, the program left the YMCA and moved to a temporary location on the south side of Syracuse, where English managed to find a rent-free apartment. Unfortunately this is located next door to a known drug addicts' hangout. But the organization continued to meet and to "hustle" for funding and a supportive agency. It was finally successful during the summer of 1972, when Task Force, a group of black businessmen, provided administrative backing.

Members of RESCUE explain the opposition by claiming that existing drug agencies feel threatened by a new group and are afraid of losing their patients and their funding. "If RESCUE works out, they would be put out of business." They also believe that white people resent black people who try to help themselves. They are sure that if they are successful someone else will try to control their program. "The idea will be snatched away." "It is just one more example how people try to take things away from black guys."

Other factors, both personal and ideological, contributed to the opposition. English had a long and sordid history during his twenty-three years of addiction in Syracuse, including nine arrests. Well known in the community, he was labeled an addict and criminal; few would believe that he had changed. And despite the obvious organizational ability of English and several others who were active in RESCUE, their limited formal training and the fact that they were nonprofessional former heroin addicts evoked the skepticism of professionals in other rehabilitation agencies. Another source of opposition was the general mistrust of

methadone maintenance. In the eyes of law-enforcement and community people as well as of DEN
members, RESCUE was composed of addicts with all
the unsavory characteristics associated with the word.
Feeling this pressure, John English requested to be
detoxified. The methadone program cooperated, decreasing his dosage over a period of two months, but
after three weeks of abstinence he returned for
methadone.

Project RESCUE has become the focal point of the
concern in Syracuse with the issues raised by the
methadone maintenance program. As an additional
competitor for scarce resources, it also poses a threat to
existing programs. Moreover, the organization is a
potential political force. If, through regular discussion of
their dissatisfactions about procedures in the methadone
program, patients begin to develop a common perspective, RESCUE can become a source of social strength
and a base from which to impose its influence on the
rehabilitation process.

Meanwhile, in October 1972, the methadone program
itself finally received some funding from the state but
only to carry it through April 1973. NACC auditors
argued that too much money was being spent per
patient, prompting a staff member to quip, "The NACC
would like us to be a lemonade stand." The number of
patients is about the same; the program remains
invisible in Syracuse with few new admissions and weak
support from other institutions. Its future remains
tenuous.

NOTES

[1]Everett Stonequist, *The Marginal Man* (New York: Scribners, 1937), pp. 2–3.

[2]Richard Stephens and Stephen Levine, "The Street Addict Role: Implications for Treatment," *Psychiatry* 34 (November 1971), 351–357.

[3]Earl Rubington, "Drug Addiction as a Deviant Career," *International Journal of the Addictions*, 2 (Spring 1967), 3–20.

[4]John Horton, "Time and Cool People," *Trans-action*, 5 (April 1967), 11.

[5]A study in British Columbia concluded that "relapses appear to be due to association patterns and boredom aggravated by lack of employment." William Johnston and Hugh R. Williams, "Abstinence-Relapse Patterns among Heroin Addicts Receiving Methadone Treatment on an Outpatient Basis," in NAPAN, *Proceedings,—Third National Conference on Methadone Treatment*, November 1970, p. 63. See also Alfred R. Lindesmith, *Addiction and Opiates* (Chicago: Aldine, 1968), pp. 146–148.

[6]Nat Hentoff, *A Doctor among the Addicts* (New York: Grove Press, Evergreen Black Cat Edition, 1970), p. 41. A brief review of studies relating drug taking with anti-authoritarianism and rebellious attitudes appears in Paul M. Kohn and G. W. Mercer, "Drug Use, Drug Use Attitudes and the Authoritarianism-Rebellion Dimension," *Journal of Health and Social Behavior*, 12 (June 1971), 125–131.

[7]A study of the pattern of cheating among methadone maintenance patients who had been on a program in Philadelphia at least six months indicated that the incidence of abuse of one of the detectable drugs was 82.5 percent and increased to 97.4 percent during the eight-month period of the study. About one-third of the long-term methadone patients submitted urine positives all of the time. These were not new or inexperienced patients, nor were they on particularly low doses of methadone. Moreover 53.8 percent were employed on a full-time basis. Thus the actual effects of "cheating" on the therapeutic process has yet to be determined. Charles D. Chambers and W. Russell Taylor, "Patterns of Cheating among Methadone Maintenance Patients," paper presented at Eastern Psychiatric Research Association, November 7–8, 1970 (mimeographed). See also William Dobbs, "Methadone Treatment of Heroin Addicts," *Journal of the American Medical Association*, 218 (December 6, 1971), 1536–1541.

[8]Project RESCUE proposal submitted by John English, September 22, 1971 (mimeographed).

[9]Personal interview with John English.

VI / *The Limits of a Technological Fix*

Societal and individual values are increasingly counter-poised in almost every medical act. Some rational and just order must be established between these values to ensure the good of society while safeguarding the traditional rights of the person. This is the central ethical issue before contemporary medicine. . . . Can we make optimal use of medicine as an instrument of social good without illicit intrusion on individual human rights?[1]

The remarkable proliferation of methadone maintenance programs, despite continuing resistance from those opposed to a therapy based on readdiction, reflects the strong social pressure for an immediate solution to the heroin problem. Many of the difficulties of methadone clinics are a consequence of rapid expansion in hasty response to public demands for action. Because the individual and social problems underlying heroin addiction are not clearly defined, the objectives of methadone maintenance and the appropriate means of organizing individual clinics have been controversial. Yet, owing to the growing sense of urgency concerning heroin use, there is a commitment both to increase the

availability of methadone and to find better technological solutions; indeed a congressional committee
has recommended a "Manhattan Project" to develop
"a drug which will effectively treat, prevent, or cure
heroin addiction. . . . No better source of action is
available to the country."[2]

Those working with addicts in established methadone
maintenance programs are usually aware of the limitations of the procedure and the dangers in relying on a
narrow technological approach, but in the context of
"crisis" a primary objective becomes rapid and visible
evidence of "success." Success becomes defined in the
instrumental language of statistics, in terms of reduced
crime and money saved in prison or welfare costs.[3]

Methadone maintenance has been less expensive than
other therapeutic approaches, and can provide service to
a larger segment of the addict population.[4] In addition it
draws appeal from the compelling authority of research
and the dramatic success of medical science in managing
disease. Although the program involves readdiction with
a potent narcotic, its advocates have been able to bypass
the moral and legislative restrictions on the dispensation
of narcotics by treating addiction as a medical problem
amenable to a pharmacological solution. Thus, the use of
methadone maintenance shifts control over the treatment of heroin addiction to the medical profession. This
has the enormous advantage of putting the scientific
community in touch with the problem, substituting an
experimental, humane, and progressive attitude for the
traditional punitive one. According to one Syracuse
methadone patient:

The methadone program is godsent. I been messing around with drugs for 17 years or more and for once in my life I am able to go straight ahead. I can go to bed and I don't have to worry about getting up the next day and go out and steal or break in your house or somebody else's house or con somebody out of something. . . . You can use methadone and drink some wine or some beer or use pills behind it and get tore. But if you sincerely want to leave methadone or leave drugs alone, period, and just let methadone take its course, you can just do your thing man, just like you. I mean like I don't look no different than you now and I feel good.[5]

As in many recent advances in biomedical science and technology, however, the implications of methadone maintenance extend beyond its immediate advantages. The possible long-term physiological or psychological effects, about which knowledge remains fragmentary and controversial, and the implications of social control tend to be overshadowed by the short-term social benefits and the efficiency of a technological solution.

Problems of Social Control

Eliot Freidson, a medical sociologist, warns that a movement to reinterpret human deviance as illness contributes to "strengthening of a professionalized control institution that, in the name of the individual's good and of technical expertise, can remove from laymen the right to evaluate their own behavior and the behavior of their fellows."[6] And the psychiatrist Thomas Szasz, a critic of the "mystification of man's relationship to his body in the name of scientific medicine," describing how society has moved from a theological outlook to a therapeutic one, suggests that the priest has been replaced by the medical profession. To restrict the legal dispensation of narcotics to physicians, he claims, is simply an arbitrary professional decision. "We act as if we believed that only doctors should be allowed to dispense narcotics, just as we used to believe that only priests should be allowed to dispense absolution."[7]

Control of a methadone maintenance program involves a three-way relationship between the patient, the clinic, and the government agencies that support and regulate the program. Regulatory agencies must trade off the values of careful scientific evaluation of the effects of a new agent against public demands for immediate use of a promising if incompletely understood drug. Representing societal concern with potential abuse, they also counterbalance the independent control of the physician in managing individual clinics. The physician is placed in an uncomfortable position of double agent; superimposed on his traditional ethical commitment to the individual patient is his obligation to the state, which supports and regulates clinic activities. The social pressure to increase the use of methadone as a means to reduce criminal behavior poses an additional ethical dilemma, for the physician may find himself serving society rather than the patient.[8] If legal coercion brings a patient to a clinic is it ethical to treat him? And is it ethical to demand behavior which is socially desirable as a requirement for continued treatment of the individual? The medical profession tends to resist government regulation; years of legal, political, and societal obstruction effectively precluded research in the

area of drug addiction, and persons currently working in
narcotics programs are particularly sensitive about their
autonomy. Methadone program directors seek legal
recognition of their work, yet they resist bureaucratic
regulation. Vincent Dole, for example, claims:

Our relation to other social agencies, the maintenance of
quality standards and reliable statistics, the effort to separate
medicine from politics, the rivalries and jealousies among
professionals, have always complicated the basic problem of
treating addicts. . . . So far programs have been effective
because their direction has been medical. . . . The success
of the treatment in the rehabilitation of addicts will decline
significantly if methadone programs cease to be medical
institutions and instead become the instruments of another
bureaucracy.[9]

Guarding its control over the procedures and
standards of the methadone maintenance program, the
medical community advocates of methadone resent the
"almost prohibitive" security requirements to safeguard
this drug. "The regulations read as though you were
going to protect the crown jewels."[10] Physicians regard
the power exercised by the FDA as usurping professional prerogatives and responsibility. Proposed FDA
guidelines that would exclude adolescent and pregnant
addicts from the program are resisted as a step
backward. "We'll be losing controls in one area and
gaining new controls in another."[11]

To what extent is autonomous control by the medical
profession appropriate in view of the social as well as
medical implications of methadone maintenance? The
methadone program has had several problematic charac-

teristics: the ambiguous differentiation between therapy and research, the safeguards required to minimize the possibilities of abuse inherent in the technology, and finally, the long-term relationship between the patient and clinic that is involved in methadone treatment.

Concern with control perpetuated an incongruous legal status for methadone maintenance programs: a therapy involving an estimated 65,000 persons remained labeled investigative research until April 1972. This vague differentiation between therapy and research has raised ethical problems which are not, however, unique to methadone maintenance. Earlier experiments resulting in therapeutic innovations—from the discovery of vaccination in 1798 to experimental heart transplant surgery—have raised similar problems.[12] For clinical research in therapeutic innovations usually draws upon a population of patients who are often desperate to try a new "cure." In this context, where those volunteering to be subjects stand to benefit from the experiment, the principle of voluntary and informed consent that was established to protect the subject of experimentation has a restricted meaning. This is particularly the case in methadone programs. Though participation is voluntary, the pressure bringing an addict to a clinic may come less from his own physical needs than from social and legal forces. This is most obvious in civil commitment programs where individuals voluntarily seek treatment but, once involved, cannot leave.[13] Jerome Jaffe's comments about requiring urinalysis in schools and compelling users to submit to detention and treatment, as in the military, suggest that the FDA approval of methadone maintenance as a legitimate medical treatment may encourage the end of the voluntary nature of the program.

The concern of government agencies and individual clinics with control of potential abuse is evident in the elaborate regulations, and this carries its own dangers. One lawyer has warned that "a social program promising a reduction in crime may be seized upon by those whose zeal for order can lead to all too casual disregard of the dignity and rights of the individual."[14] The precautions deemed necessary to prevent abuse—the daily urinalysis, the practice of withholding from the patient information concerning his dosage,[15] and the ability of staff members to suspend a patient for reasons defined by the program—may conflict with the patient's perceptions of his own needs and rights. These practices can be justified as medical precautions, but in the light of the patient's vulnerability through his addictive dependence on the clinic dispensing the drug, they can, even with the very best intentions, become a coercive means of control. There are no legal precedents that establish the extent to which civil rights may be violated by specific clinic practice, or by requiring an addict to enter methadone treatment. Similarly the limits of physician liability in such a program are ambiguous. Social policy, however, bears on legal issues, a point well understood by the legal profession. "Given the strong social policy in favor of medical treatment of opiate addiction, any action brought against a properly constituted and operated methadone maintenance program will have a heavy burden of persuasion."[16]

Similar problems of maintaining the rights of individuals follow from the relationship of "indefinite duration" involved in methadone treatment. The peculiar problems of long-term medical relationships are of growing importance, as illnesses such as arthritis, hypertension, and overweight increasingly become subjects of medical consideration. Doctor-patient relationships are generally based upon the expectation of short-term illness; the patient is expected to cooperate with the doctor and staff, relying on their expertise and observing the rules they set regarding his particular definable illness. Talcott Parsons defines the patient as exempt from normal responsibilities; he is in a condition that "must be taken care of . . . he can't 'help it.'"[17] Changing his condition requires the patient to seek and to cooperate with a technically competent person.

The addict's long-term association with a methadone program, however, involves him, not in terms of a limited medical problem, but as a total person; he is a participant in a long rehabilitative process and necessarily an active, highly motivated, and responsible participant. Yet, the medical model that serves as the basis for the program defines the patient as ill and therefore relieved of individual responsbility, unable to manage his own problems. These assumptions are reinforced by the stereotype of addicts as childlike and irresponsible; they motivate many of the program precautions such as the daily requirement to urinate on demand and under observation.[18] And they perpetuate the use of pejorative labels such as "cheating" to describe the continued use of narcotics by those unable to fully adapt to the demands of the program. The assumption of irresponsibility can strengthen the very dependence that may originally have led the patient to addiction.[19]

The Effects of Opposition

Heroin addiction is both an individual and a social problem, and attempts at solution are complicated by its relationship to dominant cultural values and their manifestation in past ways of dealing with the problem. Social ambivalence toward a therapy based on readdiction has several implications for methadone maintenance programs. Continued opposition has left them vulnerable to political and economic pressures that are reflected in erratic funding tied to political contingencies. And opposition has also influenced the relation of individual methadone clinics to their communities, often obstructing useful cooperation with police, employment services, training programs, hospital administrations, and other rehabilitation agencies, each with their own perspective on the appropriate way to deal with addiction. As methadone treatment programs rapidly increase, political considerations, erratic funding, and the tendency to avoid confronting the larger social implications of heroin addiction tend to limit the full program of rehabilitation intended by those who first developed the technique. While the pharmacological aspects of the process may achieve certain ends, the more costly but crucial aspects of social rehabilitation are neglected. Methadone maintenance programs cannot deal with the boredom experienced by their patients nor with the absence of a sense of personal control and meaningfulness in their lives.

As a consequence of continued ambivalence toward a readdiction therapy, methadone maintenance programs face a dilemma. Focusing on a technique to change the life style of its patients, the programs are based on the questionable assumption that options are available to these addicts. The programs intend to encourage behavior consistent with the dominant norms of society (order, regularity, responsibility, regular employment); they expect that the addict as a patient will take his medicine and, once his physical needs are relieved, will return to the community as a productive citizen. And they assume that he can manage without the euphoria that had once helped him to deal with physical and emotional problems. But a change in life style requires a new supportive social base to replace the old one. Studies of persons with mental disorders, for example, indicate that the success of an ambulatory patient depends on the willingness of a community to provide a positive social role for him.[20] While some middle-class methadone patients may find employment, others have more difficulty:

I feel good about myself and am really trying to get myself together and really am anxious to go out there and do my thing and find a place where I can do my thing . . . and be a contributing member of society. I'm hurt by people who, innocently perhaps, don't accept me. That I am a freak. Now in a sense I am a freak, but first I am a human being and I have feelings and I have applied for so many jobs and people aren't even kind enough to call up and say, "We've already hired somebody for that position" . . . after waiting a month or more for a telephone call.[21]

If they are unable to find employment, patients return to the influence of their old "friends" and continue to use illegal drugs. This process undermines the effectiveness of the programs.

For most addicts the values underlying methadone maintenance are inconsistent with continuing social attitudes toward the problem of addiction. One methadone patient explained her difficulties as follows:

I feel in some places they are afraid of me because I represent something that is a threat to them. That is a threat, perhaps, in their community . . . like their daughter. They're looking at their daughter, their son, their pupils . . . and that to see all I have gone through and have done, it is very threatening to them. I really feel I scare them. . . . One person thought that I . . . was going to be inebriated. She asked me, how could I work? She didn't know about methadone.[22]

The fact remains that the methadone patient is forced to accept the permanence of addiction and to deal with prevailing societal stereotypes that associate "addiction" with crime, irresponsibility, and violence.[23] He bears the burden of proving himself to be otherwise, a demanding order given the public emotion surrounding the problem of drug abuse and the limited options available to an "ex-addict" with few skills developed during years of addiction. His status as a methadone patient perpetuates his separation from the mainstream of society. Patients report a sense of isolation and social inadequacy; they tend to limit their relationships to other outsiders. Thus, the prospects of integrating a methadone patient into society are less promising than many programs suggest. In fact, methadone may be merely creating marginal men, isolated from their own communities, as well as stigmatized by the larger society as a threat to social order.

This uneasy situation is in a sense the result of the fragmentation that is characteristic of a technological approach; an instrumental method which deals with problems by breaking them down into manageable components. The physiological needs of the addict are indeed the most manageable of his problems, and methadone maintenance is important as an effective and inexpensive means to ease his condition. Redefining addiction in pragmatic terms as a physiological problem amenable to a medical solution parallels similar trends in the treatment of mental illness and, to some extent, criminal behavior.[24] In lieu of more basic solutions, the use of drugs to help control symptoms has had humane consequences, making possible, for example, a dramatic reduction in the number of people requiring institutionalization. But methadone maintenance, like other technical procedures, necessarily presupposes a well-defined problem; it does not adequately reflect the existing uncertainty about the causes, the character, and the long-term impact of narcotics addiction. Nor does it take into account the ambiguous social response which limits the options of addict-patients. Thus, while methadone maintenance is an economical solution for some of the social difficulties caused by heroin addiction, responsible for a significant decrease in criminal activity among, those associated with a clinic, it remains problematic. The danger lies not so much in the possibilities of abuse as in the societal tendency to support a drug-oriented, "tranquilizing" approach to troublesome social problems and to avoid confronting the less manageable but more fundamental questions.

The long-term success of rehabilitation efforts will hinge on public willingness to bring addicts into the larger society. In order to ease the problem of addict-related crime, this may involve making methadone more readily available to those who will not otherwise seek help. The system of dispensing methadone, however, must avoid humiliating controls which perpetuate mistrust and addict dependence. In the short run, it may be necessary to accept the fact that there will be methadone abuse; in any case, even illegal use of methadone serves to reduce the heroin needs of street addicts. More positive rehabilitation measures, however, should also involve extensive support of drug-free programs including self-help efforts. They will require continued programs to introduce addicts and former addicts into educational, recreational, and employment programs that are not oriented exclusively to the addict, thus breaking the cycle of social isolation. The risk inherent in the very success of methadone maintenance as a short-term solution lies in diverting attention from the fact that many heroin users become addicts as an adaptive response to real and overwhelming social or psychological difficulties that cannot be resolved by a simple technological fix.

NOTES

[1]Edmund D. Pelligrino, "Physician, Patients, and Society: Some New Tensions in Medical Ethics," in Everett Mendelsohn, O. P. Swazey, and I. Taviss, eds., *Human Aspects of Biomedical Innovation* (Cambridge: Harvard University Press, 1971), p. 77.

[2]House of Representatives, Select Committee on Crime, *A National Research Program to Combat the Heroin Addiction Crisis*, House Report 92–678, November 18, 1971, pp. 19–21.

[3]Proponents of methadone often talk about it as a way "to survive." For example, Jerome Jaffe, in an Associated Press interview, noted that "we're surviving with methadone and it's useful." Reported in Ithaca *Journal*, November 13, 1971. Several analysts suggest that the dimensions of public concern have been disproportionate to the actual problem. Nine million alcoholics responsible for a considerable proportion of the annual automobile deaths have, in contrast, been neglected. See Paul Ramon and Harrison Trice, *Spirits and Demons at Work: Alcohol and Other Drugs on the Job* (Ithaca: New York State Industrial and Labor Relations Press, 1972) and Health Policy Advisory Committee, *Bulletin*, June 1971.

[4]In a study of technological solutions, Amitai Etzioni and Richard Remp draw an analogy between the search for technological means to provide social services and the technology of mass production. Both are efficient, increasing output at lower cost with reduced manpower. See "Technological Short-Cuts to Social Change," *Science* 175 (January 7, 1972), 31–38.

[5]From an interview conducted by Michael Reagen in "Ideas about Drug Abuse: Proceedings from the Institute for Drug Education at Syracuse," Continuing Education Center, Syracuse University, 1971 (mimeographed).

[6]Eliot Freidson, *Profession of Medicine* (New York: Dodd, Mead, 1970), p. 250.

[7]Thomas S. Szasz, "The Ethics of Addiction," Paper at the 24th Annual Meeting of the American Psychiatric Association, May 3–7, 1971 (mimeographed), p. 7.

[8]A discussion of some of the ethical issues posed by methadone maintenance can be found in James F. Maddux, M.D., "Methadone and Medical Ethics," in NAPAN, *Proceedings*, 1972, pp. 265–267.

[9]Vincent P. Dole, M.D., "Delivery of Large Scale Treatment," in NAPAN, *Proceedings*, 1970, and Vincent Dole, M.D., "In the Course of Professional Practice," *Journal of Medicine*, 65 (April 1, 1965), 930.

[10]Letter to tthe Editor from Philip Kaufman, M.D., *New York Times*, January 10, 1972.

[11]Barry Ramer, M.D., quoted in *Medical World News*, March 17, 1972, p. 54.

[12]Francis D. Moore, "Therapeutic Innovation: Ethical Boundaries in the Initial Clinical Trials of New Drugs and Surgical Procedures," *Daedalus*, Spring 1969, 502–522.

[13]Lois Chatham, in *Proceedings*, 33rd Annual Meeting of the Committee on Problems of Drug Dependence NRC-NAS-NAE Division of Medical Science, Toronto, Canada, February 16–17, 1971 (mimeographed).

[14]Paul D. Gewirtz, "Methadone Maintenance for Heroin Addicts," *Yale Law Review*, 78 (June 1969), 1210.

[15]Louis Lasagna discusses the advantages and ethical problems of withholding information in Mendelsohn, *op. cit.*

[16]Arthur N. Frakt and Andrew K. Dolan, "Program Liability to Third Persons for Injuries Caused through Methadone Program Operations," in NAPAN, *Proceedings*, 1972, p. 235.

[17]Talcott Parsons, *The Social System* (Glencoe, Illinois: The Free Press, 1951), pp. 436ff.

[18]Frances Rowe Gearing notes that this procedure "has increased my admiration for those who can urinate on demand in the presence of an 'observer.' To the best of my knowledge no group of patients with any other medical problem are required to submit to this 'screening' procedure." Frances Rowe Gearing, M.D., "People versus Urines," in NAPAN, *Proceedings*, 1972, pp. 325–326.

[19]See William R. Rosengren and Mark Lefton, *Hospitals and Patients* (New York: Atherton Press, 1969), pp. 197–198; Eliot Freidson, *Patients' Views of Medical Practice* (New York: Russell Sage Foundation, 1961); and Howard J. Osofsky, in "The Walls Are Within," Irwin Deutscher and Elizabeth J. Thompson eds., *Among the People: Encounters with the Poor* (New York: Basic Books, 1968), pp. 239–258. They each discuss the problem of powerlessness of the patient in the medical relationship, noting especially the barriers between physician and low-status patients who are less likely to have as meaningful a doctor-patient relationship as are higher-status patients.

[20]M. W. Susser and W. Watson, *Sociology in Medicine* (London: Oxford University Press, 1971), pp. 193ff.

[21]From an interview conducted by Michael Reagen, *op. cit.*

[22]*Ibid.*

[23]Erving Goffman indicates how the identity of an individual becomes permanently marred by a past stigmatized role in *Stigma* (Englewood Cliffs, N.J.: Prentice-Hall, 1963).

[24]The dangers implicit in the spiraling tendency to use drugs as a way of solving problems and influencing human behavior has been well documented. See Henry L. Lennard *et al.*, *Mystification and Drug Misuse* (San Francisco: Jossey Bass, 1971).

A Note on the Program on Science, Technology, and Society

The Cornell University Program on Science, Technology, and Society is an interdisciplinary program for teaching, research, and increased public understanding. It evolved from a concern with how scientific discovery and technological innovation are changing economic and political institutions and are altering the values that influence social behavior. The program is funded by the National Science Foundation, the Sloan Foundation, the Henry Luce Foundation, and Cornell University.

This book is the fourth in a series developed within the program to provide information on scientific and technological advances and on the ways in which important decisions about them are made. Each study deals with a specific case selected to reveal the complexity of situations in which the problems and challenges of technology are an issue, and each study treats in detail the broader implications of the individual case.

A number of common themes are emphasized throughout the series: the use of science and technology to meet public needs, incentives and constraints on the direction of scientific and technological development, and the control of unintended and undesirable consequences of science and technology.

The social and political behavior of various groups are considered in relation to each of these themes. The groups include scientists and technologists in the political-governmental system acting in situations which carry them beyond their technical expertise; legislators and policy makers, forced to make decisions often on the basis of inconclusive evidence; and the public, concerned with the implications of technology, whose interest and activities are likely to bear increasingly on public policy.

FRANKLIN A. LONG, *Director*

RAYMOND BOWERS, *Deputy Director*

Abbreviations

AMA—	American Medical Association
BOCES—	Board of Cooperative Educational Services
BNDD—	Bureau of Narcotics and Dangerous Drugs
DEN—	Direction and Education of Narcotics, Syracuse, New York
FDA—	Food and Drug Administration
HEW—	Department of Health, Education, and Welfare
IND—	Investigative New Drug
NACC—	Narcotics Addiction Control Commission
NAPAN—	National Association for the Prevention of Addiction to Narcotics
NDA—	New Drug Application
NIMH—	National Institute of Mental Health
NRC—	National Research Council of the National Academy of Science
OEO—	Office of Economic Opportunity
WHO—	World Health Organization

INDEX